REDUNDANT SPACE — A PRODUCTIVE ASSET:
converting property for small business use

Howard Green is a lecturer in National and Regional Planning and Employment Policy at Leeds Polytechnic. His research interests include small firms and development issues. He runs several courses for professionals on property, small firms and property conversion, and has written numerous articles on small businesses.

Paul Foley is a lecturer in the Department of Town and Regional Planning at Sheffield University. He has written and undertaken research in the field of small business property, and small business performance and industrial regeneration. He has acted as a consultant to several authorities on economic issues and building conversion.

REDUNDANT SPACE — A PRODUCTIVE ASSET:
converting property for small business use

HOWARD GREEN and PAUL FOLEY

Published on behalf of the Small Business Research Trust

Harper & Row, Publishers
London

Cambridge
Mexico City
New York
Philadelphia

San Francisco
São Paulo
Singapore
Sydney

First published 1986
Harper & Row Publishers Limited
28 Tavistock Street
London WC2E 7PN

British Library Cataloguing in Publication Data
Green, D.H.
    Redundant space : a productive asset : converting property for small business use.
    1. Buildings — Great Britain — Remodelling for other use 2. Construction industry —
Great Britain 3. Small business — Great Britain
    I. Title   II. Foley, P.D.
    690'.24   TH3411

    ISBN 0-06-318344-7

Typeset by Burns & Smith, Derby
Printed and bound in Great Britain
by Butler & Tanner Ltd
Frome and London

Contents

List of Tables

List of Figures

Preface

The rapid restructuring of British industry has left a legacy of redundant and underused premises throughout the country. Employment regeneration policies stress the role which small business can play. Research in the past has demonstrated how the supply of appropriate premises has been a major constraint on the growth of small firms. This book shows how redundant and underused premises can be converted for small business use, to the mutual advantage of developer and small business. On the basis of experience of over one hundred developments, the authors outline systematically the approaches which can be taken to conversion and subdivision and the pitfalls to be avoided.

The book is intended to provoke action based on informed decision making in which problems can be anticipated and pitfalls averted. It is written primarily for businessmen or smaller developers who want to become involved in the development of small business accommodation. It will be equally applicable to the local authority, enterprise agency or small business assistance groups which want to convert or subdivide property. Many of those who advise small business such as small business counsellors, accountants, solicitors and those running courses for business will find the book useful as it highlights the need to think creatively about property and the position of property within a company's balance sheet. In addition, the various professionals within the property industry, estate agents, architects, surveyors, planners and building inspectors, will find that the book helps them piece together the development process of converting and subdividing space for small business.

Acknowledgements

We would like to thank the many individuals, too numerous to name, who have helped us during our research and consultancy on conversion and subdivision. Their many experiences have provided a rich source of practical advice.

We would also like to thank the Small Business Research Trust for funding the original pilot survey, *Putting Spare Space to Work*, and for part-funding the research for this book.

Chapter 1

Introduction

Background

The amount of unused commercial and industrial floorspace in the United Kingdom has increased dramatically in recent years. Buildings have become vacant as businesses have failed and many companies which continue to trade have contracted, leaving large areas of underused floorspace within their premises. This situation is illustrated by the fact that there are over 34 million square feet of vacant premises in London and over 30 million square feet vacant in Greater Manchester and West Yorkshire. At the same time output from many companies in the UK which continue to trade has declined. In 1985 53 percent of companies surveyed by the CBI were working below capacity. This has undoubtedly led to an increase in the amount of unused floorspace within many companies. Associated with this increase in redundant floorspace and fall in productivity has been a rise in unemployment.

By converting and subdividing these areas of redundant or underused space into small business premises, several different groups, including businesses, local authorities and communities, have been able to benefit from this gloomy situation. Considerable financial returns have been obtained at many conversion schemes in the private sector. Equally the subdivision of unused areas of premises has provided many companies with a regular income and a source of business diversification and survival.

Two main factors account for the success of the majority of conversion and subdivision schemes. Firstly, these types of development can often be undertaken relatively cheaply. As the case studies show (see Chapter 10) development costs are often lower than £3 per square foot. Consequently they provide small business premises which are very competitive in comparison with the other types of small business accommodation currently available. Secondly, small businesses are a growth sector of the economy and in many parts of the country small business units are in great demand. Between 1980 and 1984 there was a net increase of about 140,000 small businesses in the UK (over 10 percent of the UK total). As a result of these two factors, demand for small business units by conversion and subdivision is particularly buoyant.

It might be thought that the larger property developers will be reaping these rewards. For the most part it is a market which they have been reluctant to enter because of the increased management time, costs and risks which are normally associated with small business units. In general it is the smaller business and other organizations with little prior knowledge of property development who have become involved in these activities. Examples have included the entrepreneur 'with an eye for a business opportunity' who may purchase a 'bargain' property and convert it into small business units. Businesses, realizing they are paying rates, insurance, maintenance, heating, lighting and either rent or a mortgage on their excess floorspace, have returned this space to productive use by subdivision; entrepreneurs have even seen the opportunity of developing churches, schools and mortuaries into small business accommodation. If there is sufficient demand most buildings or areas of unused space can be developed into small business units. The conversion and subdivision of property is not new. Because of an increase in redundant space available for conversion, the growth of the small business sector and the prevailing enterprise culture, the number of completed schemes has, however, increased significantly in recent years.

The activities involved in converting and subdividing premises are broadly similar: both usually require market research to assess the types of units which the local market requires, the construction of partition walls and doorways, liaison with local officials, and the marketing and management of the premises. Until now developers have undertaken these activities with little guidance available, learning from their mistakes and overcoming various difficulties to create a successful development. This book draws on the experiences and difficulties of developers who have converted and subdivided property. The tips and advice based on their experience will give all those considering conversion or subdivision a better understanding of the benefits, problems and pitfalls involved in a successful development.

The book is intended to provoke action based on informed decision making in which problems can be anticipated and pitfalls averted. It is intended primarily for businessmen or smaller developers who want to become involved in the development of small business accommodation. It is equally applicable for local authorities, enterprise agencies or other small business assistance groups which want to undertake these activities. Many of those who advise businesses, such as small business counsellors, accountants, solicitors and those running courses for businesses, will find the book useful as it highlights the need to think creatively about property and the position of property within a company's balance sheet. In addition, the various professional groups within the property industry, estate agents, architects, surveyors, planners and building inspectors, will find that the book helps them piece together the development process of converting and subdividing space for small businesses. Each will not find an exhaustive coverage of their own specialist area, but they will see how it forms part of the overall framework.

What is conversion and subdivision?

A wide range of approaches can be taken in reusing buildings to provide small business accommodation. Although the activities involved are similar, two broad categories of development can be identified. These are discussed below.

Converting property

Conversion is the process by which a company, individual or group acquires a building and converts it into one or more units of small business accommodation. Many different approaches to development can be taken. Equally, a variety of developers may be involved in these activities. Approaches to development include the following.

Speculative development for rent or sale Some developers, who perceive a lack of small business units in their local area, purchase properties and convert them into small business accommodation. These units are then sold or leased commercially, providing a profitable return on the investment. Until recently this type of development was primarily undertaken by small-scale property developers, but more recently many different groups have undertaken these activities. Local authorities and other organizations assisting small businesses have increasingly become involved in the conversion of redundant properties. Some builders have purchased buildings and provided work for an otherwise unproductive workforce by converting them in 'slack periods' when they have no other contracts. Some small businesses have seen conversion as a useful form of diversification from their main activities. Several businesses and builder/developers have purchased property for conversion towards the end of the financial year as a means of investing surplus finance which would otherwise be regarded as profits and liable to taxation.

Businesses converting for their own use Some businesses unable to find suitable accommodation for their own activities have purchased redundant buildings and converted them into premises meeting their exact requirements. The conversion of schools or farm premises into industrial units is a common example of this activity. Many churches have been refurbished to provide excellent office or retail accommodation.

Businesses converting for part own use The purchase of a building for conversion is becoming increasingly popular for businesses wishing to relocate and at the same time diversify their activities. Many expanding businesses requiring new accommodation have purchased property larger than they require and have converted the surplus floorspace into small business units. These newly created units are then leased and provide a regular source of income for the company and a method of business diversification.

The opportunities and benefits of conversion are considerable. The present depressed state of the economy has produced a flood of industrial and commercial property suitable for conversion. As well as these more obvious types of property, such as old mills and warehouses, there is a variety of other buildings such as breweries, churches, gasworks, schools and hospitals with potential for conversion. In the past, only older property has been regarded as suitable for conversion. However, the recession and restructuring of the last few years has widened the range of buildings to include many modern properties. For instance in London Bernard Thorpe and Partners found that 69 percent of vacant space was built since 1970, much of which will never be reused in its existing form. Although the market for smaller units has remained buoyant, the industrial and commercial market in general is depressed and medium and large properties are increasingly difficult to let or sell. Consequently the real price of these properties has fallen. A 'buyer's market' now exists in many parts of the UK for larger premises. Property 'bargains' can be obtained relatively easily. These circumstances have provided the opportunity for developers to purchase larger units relatively cheaply to convert into the smaller units which the market requires.

The types of buildings available for conversion, their potential for reuse, and the demand for small units are not evenly distributed throughout the UK. Particular local circumstances will always determine the potential, demand and success of any conversion scheme. Full details of how to analyse local demand and the potential of a building for conversion are given in Chapters 3 and 4 respectively.

Subdividing property

The subdivision process enables businesses with excess floorspace to lease their underused space to other businesses. The level of subdivision can vary considerably. The most informal of these arrangements involves leasing a small area in the corner of a factory or office with a workbench or desk to another business – these are often called 'rent a bench' schemes. More formal schemes involve the construction of walls, doorways and toilets to create self-contained subdivided units. Subdivision is appropriate to both declining and expanding companies which have surplus floorspace. Many highly productive companies have large areas of unused space. Expanding companies find that technological innovation and investment in new plant and machinery reduces space requirements whilst achieving increased production levels.

Many businesses store machines and other items of equipment which are never likely to be used again. These often consume large areas of floorspace. Whilst this space may be required for the future development and expansion of the business, it may be more appropriate to subdivide and return it to productive use in the short term. Unused space creates a drain on the company's financial resources without producing any return. Costs such as rates, insurance, maintenance, heating, lighting and rent or mortgage repayments are still payable on this floorspace.

Conversion and subdivision is more feasible and advantageous to the owner-occupier. Many leases do not permit tenants to subdivide or sublet premises. Some tenants have persuaded their landlords to rewrite leases allowing them to create smaller units. There are two advantages for the landlord. Firstly, their premises are converted, at no cost to themselves, into the size of units currently required by the market. Secondly, they do not have the problem of finding another tenant if the existing occupant has to move or fails due to the financial burden which excess space creates.

Chapter 2

The Argument for Action

The motives for the provision of small business units by conversion and subdivision will vary between the various development agencies involved. This chapter examines these motives and associated rewards and assesses the potential, both physical and human, for conversion and subdivision within the developer's own organization. Whilst the predevelopment appraisal is approached from a business viewpoint, many of the items discussed will be equally applicable to a wider range of development agencies.

The benefits of conversion and subdivision

A move into property management is usually viewed as a quantum leap in business practice by businesses and many of the other groups considering conversion or subdivision. A fear of the 'unknown' and concern about high costs are frequently quoted as reasons for rejecting even the possibility of development. There are considerable advantages for all the various groups involved in a conversion or subdivision scheme. Different groups will undertake development for contrasting reasons. The property developer or small businessman may have financial priorities, conservationists may be more interested in preserving the building, and local authorities may share both these goals but also be concerned to support small business growth and employment creation. Whichever viewpoint is taken there is undoubtedly common agreement that subdivision and conversion provide worthwhile rewards which are outlined below.

Financial gain

For the property developer or manufacturer turned developer return on the financial investment in a development is probably the most important reason for action. A number of studies have demonstrated that net returns of between 15 percent and 25 percent can be achieved on conversion or subdivision projects. A study by the authors in 1982 at seven schemes found that conversion costs were about £1.50 per square foot.

Annual rental income at these schemes was about £1 per square foot. Gross returns (excluding interest charges) at these schemes varied between 26 and 38 percent per annum.

A major contribution to the cashflow of companies subdividing space can also be achieved. Unused space creating a drain on company resources can be returned to financial productive use relatively easily. A study published by the Small Business Research Trust showed average subdivision costs at six developments were about £1.40 per square foot. Average rental income from the units created at these schemes was £1.30 per square foot. Gross returns (excluding interest charges) ranged from 41 to 286 percent per annum. To the builder/developer a conversion project often provides a useful and financially beneficial way of employing workers during slack periods.

Government policy and the growth in the number of small firms in the UK has highlighted the need for small business accommodation. The construction of new small business units is usually very expensive; construction costs can be £25 per square foot or more. Consequently rents for these units are frequently high; £3 or more per square foot is not unusual. Conversion and subdivision provide a more competitive method of providing small business accommodation. Refurbishment costs (and the purchase price of buildings for conversion) are usually considerably lower than the cost of newly built units. As a result rents are often lower and more competitive than for newly built units. A recent survey by Bill Kataky showed rents at refurbished premises ranging from 35 pence to £2.50 per square foot.

The relatively low cost of these units has benefits for all the groups involved. Firstly, it is a far more cost-effective way of providing small business accommodation than the construction of new units. Secondly, because of the competitive rents it is often easier to find tenants than for other types of small business premises. Thirdly, the relatively low cost of refurbished units allows new small business start-ups to reduce their initial property overhead costs when they commence trading. Additionally cheaper units mean that less conventional users can lease space. Increasingly local clubs, organizations and community groups are taking space for their activities in converted property. There are also numerous examples of people who have been made redundant or taken early retirement and have developed a hobby away from their home by renting space in a converted or subdivided unit.

Job creation

Whilst the potential of small businesses to create new jobs has been exaggerated, converted premises undoubtedly have an important role to play in the job creation process. This role is particularly important in the inner city areas where unemployment is particularly high and there is an abundance of redundant property. In rural areas the contribution can be even more significant as planning policies frequently favour conversion over new development. In recent years many rural areas have experienced employment growth particularly in new start-ups, many of which occupy converted premises.

Environmental improvement and conservation

Vacant and redundant buildings represent a considerable waste of the nation's resources. Like most wasted resources there is an associated problem of decay and environmental degradation. Shabby, run-down buildings are typical of the more depressed inner city areas. As buildings decay neighbourhoods begin to look delapidated and visually depressing. 'Bad neighbour' industries such as car repairers, road hauliers and scrap metal merchants often begin to appear in increasing numbers. A vicious circle develops resulting in the reluctance of investors to finance development in these areas. Refurbishment or demolition are the only alternatives to redevelopment. In some cases demolition is not possible because buildings are listed (see Chapter 5). In these cases consent for demolition may be difficult to obtain. Conversion and subdivision schemes on the other hand can bring an air of optimism into an otherwise depressing environment.

Alternative approaches to conversion and subdivision

There is a variety of approaches which can be taken by developers providing small business accommodation by conversion or subdivision. Each development will always be unique. Local factors will determine the type of units which are developed and the layout and structure of the specific building will impose its own limitations. Each scheme will develop a character of its own. This diversity is often regarded as one of the appealing advantages of conversion over newly built units.

Despite the variety and diversity of schemes and developments, the following broad approaches to conversion and subdivision can be identified.

Informally divided space

It is not always essential or appropriate for a developer to undertake construction work to divide units. Construction work costs money and therefore raises rental costs. Many developers have minimised their costs by creating an 'open plan' environment. Individual spaces are delineated by informal partitioning such as furniture in office uses or a simple chalk line for industrial users. These types of development require trust between tenants and are more common at subdivisions where the tenant is a friend or colleague of the business developing the space. If mutual trust breaks down or new tenants require privacy the occupants can install partitions themselves.

Divided space

Where floorspace is subdivided by partitions or walls into individual small units, different types and qualities of unit can be constructed. It is possible to distinguish three broad types of unit which can be developed by dividing space.

Bare shell units As the name suggests, these are the most basic type of unit which can be provided. Services and facilities are kept to an absolute minimum. Electricity may only be provided to a junction box, lighting will be adequate but basic and decoration (if it exists) will normally only consist of a coat of white emulsion on the walls. Although these units are spartan some tenants prefer them. They minimize costs and ensure that the occupant is not paying for services they do not require. Tenants are also able to install services appropriate to their needs where required. Electric power points can be located to suit the business's layout and additional lighting can be located over machines and desks.

Serviced units   Serviced units are the next stage in a continuum of quality and services provided at small business accommodation. These units are finished to a much higher quality than the bare shell units. They are better decorated, with carpeted office accommodation and electrical power points distributed throughout the unit. Individual washing and toilet facilities may be provided in each unit. Telephones will be installed and there may be a central switchboard to deal with clients' telephone inquiries when tenants are out. Other services such as a central reception with typing and photocopying facilities may also be provided.

Supported units   The most highly serviced type of small business accommodation are supported units. These are particularly popular developments with local authorities and organizations assisting small business start-ups. In addition to providing good quality accommodation they allow communal access to a wide variety of services which small businesses would otherwise be unable to afford. Central reception areas providing typing, photocopying, telephone answering, telex, facsimile and other services are common. Many supported developments have a manager who will give business advice. Some schemes also hire or lend equipment to tenants.

Predevelopment appraisal

A predevelopment appraisal is essential before considering any development. It does not matter which types of unit are proposed, it is important for the developer to evaluate how conversion or subdivision fits into the overall activities of their particular business or organization. All groups must consider their strengths and weaknesses and decide whether property refurbishment is a suitable form of business development. Alternatively, if conversion or subdivision is proposed as a form of diversification they must consider whether they can combine the role of property developer with their existing production or service activities successfully.

A recent study by the authors revealed that many companies and organizations are simply unaware of the benefits which conversion or subdivision could have for their business or activities. Many of these groups have considerable physical, financial and human expertise and assets which are ideally suited to conversion and subdivision schemes. A predevelopment appraisal must consider the role of conversion or subdivision in the future development of a business or organization. The physical and human assets of a company or organization and the potential benefit of these resources in a development scheme must also be evaluated.

This section on predevelopment appraisal concentrates on the activities of businesses considering property development. Many other organizations such as local authorities, small business assistance agencies and cooperative groups will be considering conversion and subdivision against a diverse range of conditions peculiar to their own organization. The majority of their considerations will be broadly similar in style and content to the predevelopment appraisal for a business.

The current and future trading position of the business

An examination of the current and future trading position of the company is the starting point for all predevelopmental appraisals. This should assess business trends over the previous three years and the likely pattern of development in the next three years. It should be completed with the help of cashflow and business forecasts wherever possible. Look around at your industry – what are its prospects? Find out what competitors are doing and how your performance compares with theirs. Investigate the possibility of investment in new equipment. Now is a good time to evaluate technologically advanced equipment. Will it improve the position of the company and raise turnover or is it not appropriate? If the outlook is not optimistic, does this have implications for disinvestment and redundancy in the future? A realistic appraisal of the company's future must assume that any new developments start on a firm footing.

If the current position is favourable a discussion with your accountant may suggest that property development would be a useful investment.

Factors to consider   Having developed a realistic view of your organization and its future, it is time to look at the implications for space and possible changes in your demand for property.

1 Does your assessment suggest that output is growing and space needs will increase in the next five years? In this case conversion of a larger building might be an appropriate solution.
2 Does the assessment suggest a decline in space needs associated with either declining output or technological innovation? Subdivision would give security of additional income as well as retaining the property in case unforeseen changes cause output to expand in the future. Property and space are frequently the last element of company activities to be considered in business planning. Many companies assume that because they have space now they will always need it and that it will continue to play the same role in the development of the company.
3 Analyse how floorspace was acquired in the past. Was it obtained in a piecemeal fashion or as part of a planned development? Looking around industrial sites frequently shows how odd buildings have been added at various stages. These additions are often associated with particular elements of a company's development such as the adoption of a new process or development of a new product and the acquisition of new machines.
4 Is all your floorspace fully used? If not, will it come back into use as the company develops? Many companies have not realized how much surplus space they possess.

They do not see it as surplus because it has been added incrementally. They have never looked critically at space. Large parts of buildings are occupied by machines which will never be used again or which could be reorganized in a more efficient, productive way.

5 For the expanding company, expansion does not necessarily require a large increase in space. Technological innovation and investment in plant and machinery can considerably reduce space requirements whilst achieving greater output.

At this stage both the expanding and contracting company will have a clear assessment of their property needs. Companies with surplus space should assess the true cost to the company of leaving this space unused. This assessment could also be useful to companies considering acquiring space surplus to current requirements for future expansion.

Unused or poorly used space costs money. These costs include rates, insurance, maintenance, heating, lighting and either rent or mortgate repayments. Many companies regard these as general property overheads which cannot be avoided. If these costs are calculated for the entire building and then allocated in proportion to the unused space an assessment of the cost of that space can be estimated. Many companies have been surprised by how much money is being spent unnecessarily on space surplus to requirements.

Two strategies exist to overcome and avoid these costs.

1 Reduce costs Reorganize space and equipment to allow areas of redundant space to be moth-balled. A similar strategy could be used by companies buying space surplus to current need. If unused space is separated from their productive area companies can apply for a rate reduction. Under the terms of the 1984 Rating Act separate unused floorspace can be zero rated; this means rates are not payable on this space. Whilst the precise implementation of this procedure varies between local authorities, this approach can usually save all but insurance, maintenance and rent or mortgage costs.

Whilst significant savings can be made from zero rating, a redundant asset produces no income.

2 Subdivide and sublet and earn revenue Unused and underused space can be put to productive use if subdivided and sublet for small firms. A significant contribution to company cashflow can be achieved and good returns can be realized.

Evaluating human resources

Whichever strategy is adopted for a development it is vital to examine the management capabilities and expertise of your workforce. These human resources will be important in deciding who will become involved in your conversion or subdivision scheme. A careful assessment of existing resources will frequently reveal talents and experience hitherto untapped. Much of the uncertainty and costs of a development can be minimized if work is undertaken 'in house' with existing personnel. Many companies expanding or diversifying their activities by conversion have found it worth while employing someone with the relevant skills which they require. As succeeding chapters illustrate, two broad groups of skills are required to undertake and manage a subdivision project.

1 Management, administration and analytical skills These skills are required to undertake the market research, negotiate finance, obtain any permissions required, manage the construction work, and market and manage the completed scheme. Managing the development of a conversion or subdivision scheme from the inception of the idea to the final day-to-day management of a completed scheme can usually be undertaken by any competent director or manager within an existing company. The problems may be different from your normal activities but the management and organizational skills required are almost exactly the same for any other management problem. Since most of the problems and procedures likely to arise are outlined in this book the difficulties may be easier to solve than your normal activities where little help or advice may be available. The final day-to-day management of a scheme can frequently be provided by a director or manager who is approaching retirement. The role of part-time property manager often provides them with a rewarding challenge. It is worth while getting any such directors or managers involved in the scheme at an early stage to increase (and confirm) their interest and motivation.

2 Building and construction skills These skills are required to undertake any building, wiring, plumbing or constructional work at a development. They are also required to maintain a completed conversion or subdivision scheme.

The different constructional skills likely to be required are outlined in Chapter 6. Many workers within your business may have the skills required. Employees keen on 'do-it-yourself' often have a natural aptitude for all types of building or construction work. They can be a valuable asset. In most businesses the workforce is happy to undertake this work. Some union regulations may hinder such involvement; similarly individual workers may be reluctant to become involved. Development costs can be reduced substantially if you use your own workforce. A group of employees with the appropriate skills can transfer to the scheme on a full-time basis, or they could be released in slack periods during your usual activities.

Management staff with construction or maintenance experience will also be useful. They can supervise your own employees or where skills are lacking they can contact and manage groups of tradesmen.

A thorough examination of the management and skill resources of any business can often produce most of the necessary experience and personnel to embark on a conversion or subdivision scheme. Undertaking work 'in house' enables a company to reduce their development costs. It also allows them to control the pace of development and monitor development costs more closely.

Key points

1 Assess the benefits of conversion and subdivision for you. These will include:
   a financial gain
   b job creation
   c environmental improvement and conservation.
2 Analyse the approaches which you can take. These will include:
   a informally divided space
   b divided space
   c bare shell units
   d serviced units
   e supported units.
3 Assess your capability to undertake a conversion or subdivision. Include:
   a the current and future trading position of the business
   b the human resources within the business.

Chapter 3

Market Research

The prospective tenants of any conversion or subdivision will determine its success or failure. You will need to know their views and needs if your development is to be successful. It is essential, before carrying out any design or construction work, to investigate the workspace requirement of your prospective tenants. This will require market research. Work done at this early stage can save a lot of time, trouble and expense in the future. Market research should assess the overall demand for small units as well as the particular types required in the area. Because local factors will determine the type of units to be developed, careful attention must be given to local conditions.

This chapter reviews the broad patterns of demand for small industrial and commercial premises before presenting a framework within which to assess local demand.

The current level of demand for small premises

The overall national level of demand for small units is high. Between 1980 and 1984 approximately 830,000 new companies came into existence in the UK. In the same period 690,000 companies ceased trading. These figures indicate a net growth in the number of small businesses; births exceeded deaths by 140,000. It should be noted that these births were not evenly distributed geographically, they were probably greatest in the South East and in some rural areas. Many of these businesses will be actively seeking premises so that demand for units should grow.

Additionally, the high level of volatility of small businesses indicates buoyant demand. Small businesses tend to move premises quite frequently and this creates a buoyant market. Since subdivision and conversion usually create small business units where rentals are very competitive, developers can compete very effectively in the market. Chapter 8 outlines the most appropriate ways to market the units when completed.

These broad trends are supported by national government policy towards small businesses. Measures such as the Enterprise Allowance scheme, which started in March 1983, have been particularly effective in assisting new business start-ups. Even without this help many people have invested redundancy money in starting their own business. The recent White Paper 'Lifting the Burden' (Cmnd 9571) outlined a series of measures which will further stimulate the growth of small businesses and enhance the demand for small units. Growth of small businesses has been more vigorous in some sectors than others. As manufacturing industry has declined service industries have grown. Although service industries have tended to proliferate, local patterns vary. In some areas manufacturing, particularly 'craft'-oriented activity, is still buoyant.

In 1980, Coopers and Lybrand, a national firm of accountants, prepared a report for the Department of Industry which investigated the demand for small industrial premises. The report indicated that a number of indirect measures pointed strongly to an excess of demand over supply for small business premises. It suggested that the number of inquiries and applications for premises substantially exceeded the number of small units coming onto the market. It also found that there was very little difficulty in letting available factory units and small business premises, adding that whilst turnover of tenants may be high there was very little void in the market. The report also noted that demand varied geographically from region to region and locality to locality. This important caveat concerning the intensity of demand at individual localities is possibly more significant now than it was in 1980. Since that date the recession has deepened considerably and has affected some parts of the country more than others, modifying the local pattern of demand.

The supply of small business units has also altered since 1980. Both the public and private sectors have been constructing small units. Local authorities, concerned with unemployment, have tried to regenerate their local economy by stimulating the growth of small businesses. Some have included the construction of small units and workspaces as one method of achieving this aim. In 1979 the government introduced a 100 percent allowance on small workshop schemes. This gave tax reductions on money invested in these developments and encouraged the private sector to build new small units. This may have modified the market pattern described by Coopers and Lybrand. Allowances on small workshop schemes ended in April 1985 and the number of small units constructed is likely to decline as a result.

Despite changes since the Coopers and Lybrand report, the future outlook for conversion and subdivision schemes is encouraging. Continued government support to stimulate the number of small business start-ups should expand this sector of the economy. This will produce an increase in demand for small business premises. The growth in construction of new units which took place in the early 1980s is likely to decline in both the public and private sectors. The construction of small units by local authorities will be reduced by 'rate capping' and other government controls to restrict their level of spending. Private developers no longer receive the 100 percent building allowance on small workshop schemes so their incentive to build small units has also been reduced.

Although these national trends are encouraging, conditions will vary both regionally and locally. Market research is essential to investigate how these trends have affected your area.

Market research

If your small units are to be successful they must be developed in accordance with local small businesses requirements. This should ensure an adequate supply of tenants when the scheme is completed. In general terms, your market research should consider the items which you would expect a small business to examine when looking for accommodation. These will include:

location of units
size of units
uses (industry, warehousing, office or retail)
rentals charged
tenure
facilities offered (telephone, gas, electricity)
business support services.

These items form a checklist for your market research. Use this as a framework to record information gathered from the groups you will contact as part of your market research exercise; these groups are discussed at the end of this chapter. Each of the items on the checklist is described below.

Location

Demand for different types of small business accommodation can vary widely between different locations. Location is crucial to your assessment because it influences many of the other items on the checklist. If you are subdividing or converting property which you already own your location is fixed and these difficulties will not occur. If you are purchasing premises for conversion your investigation of the industrial and commercial property market will have to be more comprehensive; it will involve looking at all the items on the checklist at different locations. Developers who are free to choose the location of a property for conversion are in an advantageous position. They will be able to locate in the areas of greatest demand for small business premises. Even across relatively short distances of four or five miles the demand and supply of small business accommodation can vary significantly. During your market research make sure that you are clear about the precise locality under discussion.

Most tenants will not be prepared to have a journey-to-work time of more than 30 minutes (possibly longer in larger urban areas). Ensure that within 30 minutes' travel time of a location there is adequate small business activity to support your development. As well as broader locational decisions individual types of business are also sensitive to location. These considerations will be important in deciding which activities are feasible at a development. A final decision on what is possible at your scheme will be regulated by the planning system (see Chapter 5). An assessment of demand from different types of users is discussed later; this section examines the locational requirements of broad categories of business activity. Particularly in the small business sector there is a merging of these broad categories, for example many retail businesses now combine manufacturing and retailing at the same premises.

Retail use   Retailers are especially sensitive to location because they have to be accessible to their customers. The key ingredients for a good retail location are a high pedestrian flow and a large resident population. The importance of these two factors varies according to the type of retail outlet. Shops selling everyday necessities, such as food, newspapers or cigarettes, operate in a very competitive environment. A good location, with high pedestrian flow, will be the most important factor influencing the success of a shop selling necessities.

At the other extreme, shops selling specialist goods such as musical instruments, carpets or DIY tools will not require a prime location with high pedestrian flow. The majority of customers requiring specialist goods are usually searching for their particular services or products and will be willing to travel longer distances to acquire them. For this type of shop a large local resident population is more important than high pedestrian flow. Specialist shops need to be accessible; proximity of a car park or available car parking spaces is nearly always important.

Office use   All businesses have some form of office activity. However, the businesses considered in this section are those which specialize in office activities. Businesses such as insurance broking, management consultancy and accounting which have customers who regularly visit their premises require good pedestrian access and/or adequate car parking, Activities which have few visitors, such as invoicing or data processing, require less accessibility and car parking; they are freer in their choice of location. The design of a development which includes office accommodation should take account of customer access and the need for some type of reception facilities.

Industrial use   Most conversion and subdivision schemes include the provision of industrial accommodation. Although industrial users have fewer visitors their location can still be important. The speed and efficiency of contacts with customers and suppliers can be affected by location. Sites in the centre of a town, or a suburban or rural site on a major road or near an important road junction will provide good accessibility for the industrial user.

The size of units

Market research is needed to identify the size of units most in demand in your locality. In recent years several groups have developed small units of differing sizes. These have ranged from micro units of less than 200 square feet to the more common construction of workshop units of 500–2500 square feet. Your market research will have to identify the size of units in greatest demand in your locality.

Calculating the size of units which are in demand can be difficult. Businesses can only respond to what is available and frequently have little idea of what they really need. Consequently flexibility can often be advantageous, because it allows developers to provide units of differing sizes. The appropriate range to develop will be shown by market research. A miscalculation in your assessment of the size of units which the market requires can be overcome by using flexible methods of construction. These methods allow the walls or partitions of units to be moved relatively easily. As well as allowing for mistakes in market research this can sometimes provide flexibility if your tenants want to expand or contract in size in the future – an important consideration for many small businesses because relocation is costly, time-consuming and disruptive. Their decision to locate in your development may be encouraged by the flexibility you can provide.

Types of business likely to occupy a development

It is important to find out the types of businesses which are likely to require premises. Industry, office or retail uses will each have different requirements for premises and support services. They will also be willing to pay different levels of rent. This will be an important consideration when preparing a feasibility study (see Chapter 4).

It is important to be clear about the different types of users and the units they require during your market research discussions. Ask the people you talk to to consider all activities: industrial, office and retail uses. Try to examine demand for premises from as many different business activities as possible. A void in the local market may only be recalled or become apparent if you suggest the particular area of business first.

Having a variety of different business activities helps to build the character and image of a development. It also provides the opportunity for businesses to trade amongst themselves and increase or stabilize their prospects. The availability of businesses such as carpenters, metal workers, designers, caterers, printers and accountants provides an appropriate mix for intertrading. Tenants have immediate 'on site' access to these skills and the businesses providing the particular activity can pick up a considerable amount of 'extra' trade.

Rental levels

Rental charges for small business accommodation are usually variable and it is possible to encounter large differences in price for premises of broadly similar size and quality. It is particularly important to investigate the local industrial and commercial property market thoroughly before making any final decisions about the rental level you will be able to charge.

The way in which prices are quoted can vary considerably. Sometimes only rents are quoted, more often rent and rates are both included in the figure. If you are examining premises with associated services such as secretarial assistance, typing, telex or cleaning, find out whether these items are included in the rental price of the premises. It is also advisable to find out the cost of these additional services. Some developers overcharge for services; if you can undercut them you may provide a more competitive development. Ensure that the rent you are quoted is a standard price and not an introductory offer. Some premises are offered at low rents for an initial period before rising to a standard rental level later.

An assessment of rental levels in your locality will provide the basis for determining the feasibility of a development. Most developers attempt to obtain a return on the money they spend on a conversion or subdivision within three to seven years of its development. In simple terms this means that they will only spend between three and seven times the amount of expected annual rental income on converting or subdividing premises into small business units (further details of how rental figures are used in a financial feasibility study are given in Chapter 4).

During the examination of rental levels you will learn a lot about how property is promoted and the different ways in which rents can be charged. It is worth taking a few notes on your experiences and the 'tips of the trade' you detect; they will be useful later in promoting your own property.

Tenure

There are many different types of tenure which can be adopted for the small units created by conversion and subdivision. These range from selling the freehold rights on a property to short-term licences. Further details are given in Chapter 9. Market research will reveal the popular types of tenure in your area. In recent years there has been a trend towards shorter leases and 'easy in, easy out' agreements, such as licences. However, most developers prefer to have long leases so that tenants will remain at their premises for a number of years. This ensures that the costs and regularity of advertising and administering new tenancies are reduced. Even if your local market does require relatively short leases remember that it is probably more expensive, time-consuming and disruptive for your tenant to move than it is for you to advertise the property and obtain a new tenant.

It is important to investigate the precise conditions attached to tenancy agreements. Costs of services, level of repair and rent review periods are just some of the details which can vary. A fuller discussion of these issues is given in Chapter 9.

Whilst most developers prefer to lease property, some gain considerable returns from selling the freehold rights to individual units. Particular local circumstances will govern the type of tenure to adopt.

Facilities required by small businesses

The level and quality of facilities you should provide will depend on local market demand and the type of tenants you want to attract. Some facilities, such as electricity and telephones, will be required by nearly all businesses. Other facilities, such as three-phase electricity, gas, artificial ventilation, extra lighting, special floor or wall coverings, and strengthened floors to take heavy equipment, might be required by some tenants.

If you intend to attract certain types of tenants it is important to investigate the facilities which they require. If you are in doubt about providing any of these it is best not to install them until they are needed. If tenants want particular additional facilities it is possible to allow them to install these under the terms of the lease. If they are unwilling to pay for these themselves it is possible to offer a period of reduced rents or 'rent free'.

Business support services

There is a growing tendency at some conversion and subdivision schemes to provide a range of business support services. The type of services offered might include a central reception with telephone answering, mail distribution, typing, telex, photocopying, book-keeping and accounting services. The idea behind the provision of these services is that individually small businesses either cannot afford them or they do not use them enough to make their purchase worth while. Market research should investigate which of these services are available and their level of use. Frequently services are provided but remain unused. Distinguish which services are most worth while. Remember that they must be appropriate to the type of tenants you intend to attract.

Do not base your market research solely on the services available locally. The adoption of a new or different service may help to attract tenants. For most services there is a threshold of usage which is required to make their provision economically viable. Problems have arisen when tenants have become disgruntled at paying for a telex machine or other service which they never use. Careful market research will avoid the pitfalls of providing inappropriate services.

Undertaking market research

Market research is concerned with investigating two areas. Firstly, you should find out what type of premises the small businesses in your locality require. Secondly, you will need to ensure there is sufficient demand for this type of premises to make its construction worth while. There are many groups and individuals who can help in your assessment of the small business industrial and commercial property market. Some of the groups you contact will also be useful in marketing your completed development. The main groups to contact are listed below.

Industrial development officers

Local authority industrial development officers should have a good understanding of the local property market. They are approached by many businesses asking for advice about property or looking for premises. They will have a clear understanding of the types of property most in demand in their local area.

Local authority estates departments

In recent years some local authority estates (or industry and estates) departments have become increasingly involved in the management of small business units. This experience will enable them to advise about the gaps in their local industrial and commercial market.

Local business clubs

Small business clubs, associations and Chambers of Commerce and Trade provide a forum for businesses to exchange ideas, problems and common interests. Contact the committee members of these organizations or their full-time employees. They will be well acquainted with the local property market and the property problems and difficulties encountered by their small business members.

Enterprise Agencies and small business advice groups

Both these groups are visited by small businesses seeking help and advice. Many of these inquiries will be problems concerning property. Some have lists of small businesses looking for property. They may be willing to give the names of these companies so that you can discuss your joint property interests. Some groups are concerned with confidentiality and will not release the names of clients.

Local newspapers

Local newspapers are one of the most useful sources of market research information. Look at both the 'vacant property' and 'property wanted' columns. Companies advertising in the 'property wanted' columns can be contacted for further details of what they require. They may also be willing to give you their views on the local property market.

Developers advertising property, particularly the type you may be developing, will be useful. You can ask what level of response they had to their advertisement. When these units later become occupied approach the new tenants. Find out how many similar units they considered. They should have a clear idea of the current state of their section of the small business property market.

Estate agents

Not all estate agents deal with industrial property. Agents have been more willing to promote small units in recent years. Some agents only promote the more expensive properties from which they receive higher commission. The authors have found that they are more optimistic about the potential benefits of new developments than they are about conversion or subdivision schemes. It is often better to approach agents as if you are looking for a particular type of property. This will reveal a more accurate picture of the market.

A local view

A simple look around your locality will provide a good indication of the state of your industrial and commercial property market. Frequently smaller units are only advertised by billboards. If premises similar to the type you will be developing are available ask nearby companies or the landlord how much interest has been shown in the property.

These seven sources should introduce you to the key people concerned in the industrial and commercial property market. Most groups will be very willing to talk to you. Some may have to be flattered or cajoled. When talking to some rival developers or landlords you may have to be humble or 'thick skinned' to resist their contemptuous remarks. Be persistent and overcome these difficulties. Your conversion or subdivision will only be successful if it provides the type of units which your local property market requires; all these people will ensure it meets this requirement. When you visit them refer to your market research checklist and ask about all the different items it contains. Keep a written note of the types of property they think the local market requires.

Some developers totally disregard market research and prefer to use their own 'gut feelings' in designing a development. Due to luck or good judgement many of these are successful. In doing so they take considerable risks. By undertaking market research and visiting all the groups outlined earlier you can reduce these risks and increase your chances of developing a successful conversion or subdivision. Remember that if your development is not required by the market it will fail and remain empty. All your investment will have been wasted and it could cost thousands of pounds to make it successful. *Market research is essential.* It will almost certainly be the difference between a successful development and a costly failure.

Key points

1 What is the current level of demand?
2 Where is demand located?
3 What size of units does the market require?
4 What rents are currently being charged for small units?
5 What types of users require small units?
6 What types of tenancy agreements are available in the area?
7 What facilities are required?

Chapter 4

Identifying and Assessing Buildings for Conversion and Subdivision

In Chapter 1 two different approaches to conversion and subdivision were described:

1 A developer who is looking specifically for a building suitable for conversion. The developer may be a cooperative, local authority or private development company. The developer may also be a business looking for new premises which they can occupy and/or develop as an asset and gain rental income from tenants. In all these cases the developer will be involved in the search for a building and in assessing its development potential.
2 A businessman who already has an active business, but has space surplus to requirements. In this instance the developer is concerned with assessing the suitability of his existing property for subdivision.

Chapter 3 outlined the market research activities required to find out which types of small business units should be constructed at a development. Developers subdividing property will already have a property in which they can develop these units. Developers considering conversion will have to find a building suitable for the development of the small business units which market research has shown are required. The first part of this chapter examines the different ways in which properties suitable for conversion can be identified. This is followed by a discussion of issues more closely related to the attributes of individual buildings. Those who already have a property available for development can move to the section dealing with the building itself on page 26.

Sources of information about vacant property

There are several sources of information about vacant property in the area. These will include many of the groups you will approach during your market research. Because you are interested in buying property and indirectly helping to regenerate the local economy by providing small business units many of the official or advice agencies may be more willing to assist you in your market research and your search for suitable premises for conversion. But be careful, estate agents and other groups who gain from selling property may be overoptimistic about the demand for small units. In order to remain on your 'good side' or entice you to buy one of their properties they may exaggerate local demand and rental levels. It is sometimes better to approach them first for market research information about small units and return to them later for details about property suitable for conversion. Information about properties suitable for conversion can be gained from the following sources.

1 Local authorities

Most local authority planning, employment or estates departments keep a register of vacant property. They tend to concentrate on conventional industrial property and consequently may not include buildings which are not currently classed as industrial or commercial but which have potential for conversion. As the lists are regularly updated from information provided by both the public and private sector, they are probably the most comprehensive single source of vacant property.

The local authority education department will also be able to advise on vacant educational property.

2 Estate agents

These are the obvious source of information. Approach the larger agencies as the small ones will tend to specialize almost exclusively in residential property. Agents will often promote the most expensive property as their commission is tied to the sale price. Similarly, they will tend to offer property based on existing use, rather than future potential use. Remember to ask about other types of property.

3 Walking or driving around

In many parts of the country where large amounts of property are vacant, and where there is little likelihood of lettings or sales, owners frequently do not bother to advertise formally. The only advertising undertaken may be by billboard outside premises. Touring the area will in this instance be the most appropriate way of finding property.

4 Personal contacts

Your contacts in the business world will also be useful. Tell people what you are looking for. Contacts may be aware of suitable property; they may also warn you about particular properties which may not be the bargains which superficially they appear to be.

5 Local newspapers

Most local newspapers have sections devoted to property. Frequently they will have a particular issue each week which is accepted as the 'property day'. Newspapers are a particularly good source of less conventional property.

6 Other sources of information

A wide range of other agencies may provide information on property suitable for conversion or subdivision. Many of the major industrial and commercial companies have estates departments which will deal with vacant property within the company. Notable examples include the British Rail Property Board, NCB Enterprises (an offshoot of the National Coal Board) and BSC Industry Limited. It is always worth contacting the major companies in your area to inquire about vacant property which they may have to offer.

It is important to look beyond the conventional wisdoms concerning the types of property which may be suitable for conversion. Many people have very constrained ideas about the uses to which different buildings can be put. These views can be advantageous for the developer. If the value of a building is only associated with its previous use it is possible that conversion will use the building more productively and enhance its value. An example of this is the conversion of barns, schools and churches to small business units. Many agents regard only older industrial property as suitable for conversion. They are still confident that the large single-storey factories built since the 1960s will be sold or leased again in the future. Even larger modern factories are worth serious consideration for conversion. Frequently these may be unrealistically priced because the value is associated with their previous use before the current recession when demand for larger units was buoyant.

Searching for buildings

Any investigation of the buildings suitable for development requires a systematic process of sifting and evaluation. This process is best undertaken in three stages, to investigate:

1 cost and size
2 location and character
3 specific characteristics of the building.

Before beginning the search for suitable property it is essential that there is a clear statement of what is needed and the parameters within which the development will take place. Much of this information will be given by the market research. Other information will relate to the developer's own particular circumstances and the amount of finance available for a development (for further details about finance see Chapter 7).

1 First-stage sift: cost and size

This will be based on the initial parameters of the project and will relate to costs and size. Many buildings will be too expensive for available resources or expensive in relation to the general property market in the area. They may be too big or too small. Market research and financial constraints will have given an approximate idea of what is wanted. Do not take on more than is needed. If a freehold is required do not, at this stage, consider leasehold property.

2 *Second-stage sift: location and character of the area*

The second-stage sift can be based almost entirely on location and character of the area. Key questions to ask include:

1 Where is the site in relation to the local demand shown in the market research?
2 How far is the site from other industrial/commercial users?
3 How far is the site from the town or district centre? (Such centres may be attractive to tenants and hence influence occupancy rates, and rents.)
4 What are public transport facilities in the area like? Is it accessible for workers?
5 What plans do the local planning authority have for the area? What are the current industrial or commercial planning policies? What changes are planned for the area? Has the local planning authority designated it for industrial development and improvement? (More information on these issues is given in Chapter 5). Is it part of an Inner City Area or an Enterprise Zone? (In which case additional finance may be available. See Chapter 7.)

It is important to look at the Local Plan for the area. This is a document available from your local authority planning department which describes the character of a particular locality and the authority's future plans for the area. The Plan should be accessible and quite easily understood. If a Local Plan has not yet been written ask the planning department about the area and their possible future proposals for the locality.

At this stage make a new or revised shortlist of the sites which fulfil your requirements. It is useful to devise a very simple means of scaling each site and location based on all your considerations. Use a simple system of evaluation based on the kinds of parameters outlined below.

1 A site in an isolated area will be a security risk, it may be difficult to attract workers, particularly women, and will not pick up casual custom for the tenants.
2 A site away from public transport routes may have access problems.
3 A site near the city centre may allow a mix of uses including office use, but access may be a problem.

Do not forget that the image of an area is important. A run-down area may not be attractive to potential tenants. However, the development could be the catalyst required to encourage others to redevelop nearby buildings. Eventually the scheme could lead to the regeneration of whole run-down areas within a city. Your lead could encourage others to follow. This is a particularly important consideration in the development of some local authority and charitable schemes.

3 *Third-stage sift: characteristics of the building*

Once a shortlist of suitable sites has been drawn up, it is time to look at the buildings themselves. Whilst a site may be ideally located and set out in the context of the market research, it is the characteristics and condition of the buildings themselves which will dictate whether a site has real potential or not. Experience of subdivision shows that a number of characteristics at each site should be examined. This investigation should be undertaken by both the new developer and the business which has unused space. It will determine whether buildings are appropriate for conversion or subdivision.

(a) Site layout

Building density Is the site made up of more than one building? Single building sites, where one building covers 100 percent of the site area, make very efficient use of the land but they often generate a number of problems. The construction of walls and partitions is usually necessary to subdivide units and it is often difficult to provide adequate access, parking and loading facilities for each unit. Lower density sites, with roads or access all around a single building, or sites with several buildings are to be preferred. Lower density sites with several buildings are usually the most appropriate. Frequently individual buildings can be used as single units without any conversion work. Sites with an existing road layout or access routes between buildings allow traffic to circulate more easily.

Building size What are the floor areas of individual buildings? If the units to be created are in the range of 500–2500 square feet, this is achieved more easily in smaller buildings. In larger premises more 'juggling' and calculations are required to fit as many units into the building as possible. It is often necessary to build corridors to allow access to units; corridors are communal space for which tenants do not pay rent.

Multi-storey buildings Is the building single- or multi-storey? Single-storey buildings are far easier to convert and let because of ease of access and lack of problems associated with floor loadings and fire regulations. Floor loading capacities can be a problem in older multi-storey property especially where floors are wooden. Improving floor loading capacities can be very expensive. Their wooden construction frequently means that upper floors are unsuitable for heavier industrial use. Wooden floors in old textile or engineering works are often a major fire hazard because over time they have become impregnated with oil. Upper floors will usually command lower rentals because of the difficulties of access. Multi-storey property on sloping ground may provide the opportunity for multiple access at different levels. This will help to overcome some of the problems associated with multi-storey buildings. Roof heights can be important as very high roofs may allow the construction of a mezzanine floor for office purposes. In buildings such as warehouses and maltings floor to ceiling heights can be too low for modern standards.

Building depth What is the relationship between the width and depth of the building? These expressions refer to the external measurements of the building and its overall size; 'depth' refers to the distance of the 'centre' of the building from the nearest wall. Deep buildings often create problems in providing natural light to central areas. This may require the use of additional lighting.

Services What services are installed at different parts of the site? The existing provision of services such as three-phase electricity and toilets will greatly reduce development costs. Check that they are all in working order. Does the building have a sprinkler system in working order? An efficient sprinkler system can reduce building and fire regulation difficulties as well as insurance premiums. It will also allow a wider range of uses. However, sprinkler systems do freeze and cause water damage in unheated buildings. It is vital to protect or drain the system if construction work is taking place in winter and no heating is available.

Building condition   What is the overall condition of the building? How long has it been left unoccupied? Buildings left empty for some time with no maintenance soon deteriorate. Check roofs, especially flat roofs and valley gutters. Look for tell-tale signs of damp patches. Are there any signs of vandalism? The age of the building is not necessarily a good indicator of its condition. Many postwar buildings are built on concrete frames, with asbestos roofs, and possess steel windows. All these items have a limited life. They are very expensive to replace. Look carefully for signs of deterioration.

Boundaries   Are the current boundaries secure? Will they be adequate for incoming uses? Frequently boundary fences and walls are in a poor state of repair. Good boundaries and gates are an important part of the image of the building as well as being important for security and the prevention of vandalism. Have a good look round. Boundaries can be very expensive to repair and replace.

(b) Restrictions on the site   There may be restrictions imposed on the site or individual buildings. These arise from a variety of sources and will include:

Current planning position   Local authorities zone some areas for particular activities (see Chapter 5). If the area or building you are considering is not zoned for industrial or commercial use there may be problems in developing the site. It is important to look at the planners' long-term proposals for the area. If it is surrounded by housing there might be a problem in gaining planning permission for the development. Inquire about the uses for which the site can be developed. The existing 'use class' may allow a reasonable range of tenants or it may be necessary to apply for a 'change of use' (see Chapter 5). Investigate these areas carefully before considering the site in detail.

Preservation orders   It is surprising what an assortment of buildings now attract preservation orders or are listed as architecturally significant (see Chapter 5). These orders can restrict development and generally cause increased problems in gaining permission for a conversion or subdivision. Typically, they will hinder the reorganization of a site in which some selective demolition is required to improve site access and circulation.

Covenants   Covenants within the deeds of the property may restrict its use and prevent the kind of development you propose. Take care to check through the deeds for any restrictive covenants which may affect the development potential of the property.

(c) Circulation, access and parking   Subdivision of buildings into small units will frequently intensify the use of the site. The construction of new units will increase the movement of people and goods; this will put pressure on the circulation, access and parking facilities at the site.

Circulation   It will be vital to investigate whether there is adequate space for general vehicular circulation within the site. This will include not only cars and light vans, but large delivery lorries. Whilst circulation might have been fine for the previous use, small units create their own problems. Can new points of access be created within the building? Are there goods lifts or external goods hoists? Do they work? Will there be parts of the building to which large lorries will not be able to make deliveries? Can selective demolition alter this position?

Access Access to and from the site is one of the areas which the local planning authority will consider if planning permission is required. Increased use of the site may place greater demands on the points of access. Is current access good? Will it need improving? Can it be improved? Direct access onto main roads may be a problem. Can alternative access routes be made into side roads?

Parking Is there adequate parking space? Remember many industrial buildings were built long before car ownership was common.The use of on-street parking may no longer be tolerated by the planning authority if the use of the building changes. Tenants will require parking space both for themselves and their clients close to their premises. A visitors' car park is necessary at some developments. Can this be incorporated within the site layout?

The final shortlist

It is now appropriate to assess individual buildings bearing in mind the points already made on what to look out for in a building suitable for conversion or subdivision. To do this, make up a simple survey sheet on which to record observations about individual sites. Table 4.1 shows a typical record sheet which could be used for this purpose. Visit each prospective building and make brief notes about each aspect of the site, also give each element a score from 1 to 5, where 1 is poor, bad or inadequate, and 5 is good or highly satisfactory. For example, if the site were made up of six buildings all less than 10,000 square feet it would score 4 or 5 for both number of buildings and size of buildings. On the other hand, if it had no parking space on the site, it would score 1 for parking. This process need not take very long. In the space of a day the exercise can be completed at four or five sites. The scoring system is an aid in making a decision; it is not a decision-making process in its own right. Different groups will attach varying levels of importance to each item on the schedule. For this reason your market research results, company goals and comments about each property should be used in conjunction with the scoring system to decide which property is most suitable for development. The evaluation schedule will ensure you are considering all the important features at each property. This will assist you in creating a framework for arriving at a well-informed decision about the development potential of each site.

Companies assessing the potential subdivision of underused space can use the schedule for their existing building. Using the criteria suggested it will give a systematic evaluation of the building's potential for development. If the business is contracting on more than one site, the schedule will help determine which site has the greatest development potential.

Table 4.1 Site evaluation schedule

Address	Agent	Price ....
....	....	
....	....	

Site Characteristic	Score (1–5)	Comments
Layout		
No. of buildings		
Size of buildings		
Single/multi-storey		
Depth of buildings		
Services		
Condition		
Boundaries		
Current planning position		
– Area		
– Building		
Orders or covenants		
Site circulation		
Access		
Parking		
Total Score	**Overall Judgement**	

Some guiding characteristics of buildings

Whilst each building will be unique in its suitability for conversion or subdivision, it is possible to develop some broad generalizations about the advantages and disadvantages of different types of buildings. Some of these are noted below for three types of buildings.

1 Large warehouses and mills

These types of property may have the advantages of low price but many will have serious development problems. These will include condition, structure, floor loadings, internal access, circulation on site, location, fire risk and size. Whilst there are notable examples of warehouses and mills of over 200,000 square feet being converted for small units, the sheer size of the buildings is frequently the major obstacle to their development. In Northern England there are many mills which have been maintained to very high standards by family businesses and which are worth serious consideration.

2 Large postwar factories

Large postwar factories will have few of the problems associated with modern standards and practices (see Chapter 5). The locations will in general be appropriate to small unit development. The predominantly single-storey structures present few access or circulation problems and car parking is usually adequate. The major problems will relate to the size and shape of the buildings and the amount of internal partitioning which will be required to create small units. The subdivision may in itself create major internal access problems. This type of property is frequently unrealistically priced relative to market demand.

3 Schools

Schools are increasingly popular as basic structures for conversion to small units. The classroom layout is ideal for small units so that little internal construction is required. Playgrounds provide adequate car park space and the predominantly single-storey structures present few access- or fire-related problems. Local authority ownership can often ease the purchase and development of schools for small business units. The location of schools in residential areas can cause local planning difficulties particularly in relation to access and nuisance.

Cost guidelines

The full cost of a development will depend on the approach taken to the subdivision work itself and the condition of the building. These issues are discussed in Chapter 6. A feasibility study will give more precise figures.

Broad indications of the costs involved in developments of differing standard in the

Table 4.2   Costs and returns in conversion schemes

---

1 **Basic: private development** (complying with minimum regulations).

Development cost: £1–£1.50 per sq ft
Rental (basic):   50p–£1 per sq ft*

2 **Medium quality: private development** (satisfies all regulations).

Development cost: £3–£5 per sq ft
Rental (basic):   £1–£1.50 per sq ft*

3 **Upmarket: private development** (a high quality scheme).

Development cost: £8–£12 per sq ft
Rental (basic):   £2.50–£3 per sq ft*

4 **Local authority** (high quality to ensure it fully satisfies all regulations).

Development cost: £10–£20 per sq ft
Rental (basic):   £2.50–£3 per sq ft*

---

* All rentals are based on light industrial use and exclude rates and service charges.

same building are a useful guide to the intending developer and are illustrated in Table 4.2. It should be borne in mind that costs can vary significantly throughout the country. None of the guide figures is based on Greater London examples where figures may be significantly higher than those quoted. The purchase price of the property may similarly vary depending on the area and type of building. The figures illustrate very clearly the interrelationship between costs and rentals for the same building developed to different standards for light industrial use.

Feasibility studies

A feasibility study is essential if you are to arrive at an accurate assessment of the costs to be incurred and the overall viability of the project. A study will certainly be required if a bank or other source of external funding is to be involved. Some small developers who have undertaken this type of work before base their decisions about viability on experience gained from other schemes.

There are many approaches of differing complexity which can be used in feasibility studies. Studies can be commissioned from appropriate development and architectural consultancies. However, a simple feasibility study can be undertaken as shown in Table 4.3. Each of the items in the study will vary in importance depending on the type and level of development to be undertaken. From these figures total development costs can be calculated. In this example a net annual rent income of £9430 (£0.73 per square foot gross) would be required to service the debt of £62,870 on a commercial mortgage with an interest rate of 15 percent. Alternatively a cashflow analysis will allow you to calculate the payback period for the scheme including paying back the capital borrowed.

If the feasibility study shows an inadequate rate of return, an unacceptably long payback period or rental income below that needed to service your loan, then several alternative courses of action should be considered:

1 the mix of uses can be adjusted to raise potential rent income
2 a lower level of building works can be carried out
3 the development can be abandoned and another investigated.

If the specific development is abandoned, then it may be worth going back to the site evaluation schedule and looking at the next best alternative, which may, because of other attributes, now prove feasible.

In the case of firms with underused space or agencies who already have suitable property in their ownership, the equation may be slightly different. Here the assessment of viability may not rest simply in terms of rate of return but in alternative strategies for the building. However, unless a notional value of the building is included in the feasibility equation the scheme will usually be attractive. Even if buildings are zero rated they will require some maintenance to keep them from ultimately falling down. A company's image will not be improved if it has delapidated property. In these cases any positive return should be an attraction for subdivision of redundant space.

Table 4.3   A sample feasibility study (13,000 square feet industrial property)

Development costs

	Costs
Work on site	400
Roof repairs	2,100
External walls and windows	1,300
Plumbing and sanitary work	2,400
Electrical installations	6,200
Provision of partitions and doors	4,100
General repairs	2,000
Decoration	1,200
Contingencies (10%)	1,970
	£21,670

Professional fees

Purchase of freehold	40,000
Agency and legal charges	1,200
Total development costs	£62,870

Interest charges on loan (@ 15%)	£9,430

Minimum rent income   £9,430 or £0.73 per sq ft (gross)

Key points

1 Make a comprehensive list of buildings available.
2 Sift through the list in three stages to identify:
   a buildings which fit the basic parameters of size and cost
   b buildings which are in an appropriate location
   c buildings which have a suitable structure, layout and other attributes.
3 Undertake a feasibility study for the building selected.

Chapter 5

Gaining Approval for the Development

Introduction

The processes of gaining approval for a development and designing a conversion or subdivision are closely related. Building control officers, planners and many other groups will have to approve your design before you can begin building or construction work. For this reason information on regulations and gaining approval precedes the chapter on design, layout and construction. This will enable the reader to understand the different conditions and regulations which will have to be taken into consideration when designing a development. In reality the design process and approval process frequently take place in tandem. Before submitting plans for final approval it is often necessary to consult some of the groups concerned to clarify exactly what they will or will not allow at your development. These negotiations frequently influence the final design of a development and ensure that it receives approval.

Various pieces of legislation affect development, and several official and some unofficial bodies may be involved in the process of gaining approval. They must be consulted before any building or development work takes place to ensure that byelaws and regulations are not contravened. Each body examines proposals from a different viewpoint. Take time to explain your ideas, be patient, try compromise, learn from others, even accept some of their ideas and reservations. The groups who may need to be consulted or involved are listed below.

1 Town planning officers
2 Building control officers
3 Environmental health officers
4 'Statutory' undertakers – a formal way of saying the Gas Board, Water Board, Electricity Board and British Telecom
5 Fire officers
6 Health and Safety Executive (Factory Inspectorate)
7 The local community – including local press.

This list may seem daunting. Some of the consultation and approvals may be done automatically for the developer. The planning authority, for example, may consult environmental health officers and the Water Board in the process of giving planning approval. Many local authority departments concerned with these issues are frequently located in the same building.

Planning permission

Planning is probably the most important of the approvals you will have to obtain. Whilst all the other areas are negotiable and solutions can be found, perhaps at a cost, planning can put an absolute stop on development if the scheme does not conform to the planners' requirements. This is one area where you may need to seek professional advice from a planning consultant.

Planning controls have become a highly emotive issue in the last few years. They need not introduce problems for development if certain general principles are followed. Very useful pamphlets are provided in *Planning Permission – A Guide for Industry* and *A Step by Step Guide to Planning Permission for Small Businesses* prepared by the Department of the Environment. Both are available free from all local planning departments. All applications and inquiries relating to planning matters should normally be directed to your local district or borough council.

The need for planning permission

Deciding whether permission is needed or not can be a bewildering task. It does not have to be; the following three-stage check simplifies the problems.

Stage 1 If conversion or subdivision constitute 'development' as defined in the Town and Country Planning Act 1971, planning permission is required. Section 22 of the Act defines development as 'the carrying out of building, engineering or other operations, on, over or under land or the making of any material change of use of buildings or other land'. (Demolition is not normally regarded as development and hence does not require permission. There is, though, special control over the demolition of listed buildings or buildings in a conservation area.)

This does not appear to leave much scope. But there are one or two things that can be done which do not require permission. These include: interior maintenance, improvement and alterations, and exterior work that does not affect the external appearance of the buildings, but only if such work does not increase the size of the building below ground.

Stage 2 Some types of development are permitted and do not require permission. Even if permission is required in stage 1, some development may still be allowed without permission. Development which does not require permission includes the following.

1 An industrial building may be extended by 25 percent of its existing volume up to a maximum of 1000 cubic metres.
2 Some minor developments are allowed. These include temporary buildings, such as site huts and store sheds.

Stage 3 If the development leads to a major change of use, permission is required. Planners have divided different business activities into groups which they call 'use classes'. The different types of 'use class' are given below. Each 'use class' group permits various activities. If a property has permission for use in a specific 'use class' any of the activities which are allowed by that 'use class' can be undertaken within the property without applying for permission. It is only when an activity would require a change of 'use class' category that permission is required.

There are some exceptions: a change from 'general industrial use' to 'light industrial use' does not need permission as long as total floor space does not exceed 2530 square feet. The more relevant 'use classes' are listed below.

Class I	Use as a shop (except for those selling hot food, tripe, pets, cats-meat and motor vehicles).
Class II	Use as an office.
Class III	Use as a light industrial building.
Class IV	Use as a general industrial building.
Classes V–IX	Special Industrial Groups involving more dangerous or obnoxious industrial processes such as alkali works, smelting or plating metals, processes involving burning, industrial recovery processes (refining oils, recovering rubber and other chemicals), working with animal products (fat melting, glue making, bone grinding, etc.).
Class X	Use as a wholesale warehouse or repository.

The 'use classes' order is at present under review so it is important to check the current position with your local planning authority.

Surprising as it may seem, it may be necessary to establish what 'use' your building has permission for at present. It is one thing to be carrying out a particular activity and quite another to have established permission to do so! In such cases the permitted use will have to be established. This is called a 'Section 53 (of the 1971 Town and Country Planning Act) determination'. If in any doubt about the need for permission, get in touch with the local planning department.

Whom to contact

In most cases the local authority planning department should be contacted for permission or further advice. In some areas of the country, however, permission is either not required or is obtained from a different organization. These cases are listed below.

Enterprise Zones: Twenty-five Enterprise Zones have been established throughout the country. Their main aim is to aid industry by giving tax concessions and simplifying administrative controls. Most developments are granted automatic planning permission. There are one or two conditions and some types of development that may not be permitted. Where approval is needed, it is usually given within fourteen days (see Appendix 2 for a list of areas). Do remember all other types of approval, such as building control, will normally be needed.

New Towns: In New Towns, planning matters do not normally come under the control of the local authority. The Development Corporation is the appropriate body to contact.

If there is any doubt about the need for planning permission, get in touch with the appropriate local agency. They will help you fill in any application forms correctly and also suggest other groups who should be contacted.

Changing attitudes towards industrial and commercial applications

Attitudes towards industry are changing amongst planners, primarily because the present government and the need for jobs have highlighted the necessity for a flexible, responsive approach to industrial development applications. The ground rules for a quicker, more flexible approach were outlined by the government in 1980 and 1984 in the so-called 'Circulars 22/80 and 16/84'. The government White Paper 'Lifting the Burden' spelt out very clearly the approach which local authorities should adopt. Most planning officers will now be as sympathetic as possible to developments which aid small businesses. There is, though, considerable discretion within the planning framework and within the strategic policies of individual authorities. Attitudes towards development vary between the north and south of the country as they do between authorities in the same area. It is always necessary to consult the planners in your area. Details of the important planning circulars are included in Appendix 3.

Important planning considerations

There is a wide range of issues which the planning officers will consider when looking at proposals. Several issues which have been important at many conversions and subdivisions are discussed briefly below.

Parking Car parking requirements are determined by individual planning authorities. It is often difficult to achieve required levels of off-street (private) parking because of high site densities, especially in older industrial areas. The planning department may suggest selective demolition to create more car parking space on the site. They will look critically at the possible new levels of on-street parking created by the development.

Access to public highway The county council, which is usually the highway authority, will examine the highway implications, particularly access, of the development. Most conversions and subdivisions will generate extra traffic and the planners will need to be convinced that the existing roads are capable of handling this increase.

Use of the building The proposed use of the building has to be declared on the plan so that it can be assessed in the context of the future plans for development of the surrounding area. It is wise to check the 'Local Plan' for the area to confirm the new use is acceptable. Problems frequently arise in small unit developments where 'mixed uses' occur. These are schemes where activities such as retailing and manufacturing or offices and manufacturing take place on the same site. Whilst planners will accept the mixing of uses if they are part of the same company, they are generally far less happy if 50 percent of units are to be used for manufacturing and 50 percent for offices.

Buildings listed because of special architectural or historic interest and conservation areas   Buildings which are listed because of their special architectural or historic interest or buildings in conservation areas are subject to special control. In these cases special conditions apply and permission is required in all cases. Many developers have experienced difficulties with these controls, particularly when they have needed to demolish buildings to provide more car parking spaces and conform to parking requirements! Alterations and extensions which will affect the character of listed buildings need listed building consent even if they are permitted development and would therefore not normally require planning permission. This problem occurs far more frequently than might be expected. It is surprising how many buildings are now listed.

Planning charges

Advice from local planning officers is free but actual planning permission costs money. For instance, a change of use certificate costs £53. There is a sliding scale of fees. Broadly speaking, planning charges relate to the nature of the development. More details are given in Table 5.1. Each separate application is chargeable although it may relate to the same property, so it is vital to think carefully about the development and include everything on one application.

Table 5.1   Charges for planning approval

Full Planning Application for:	
Erection of buildings (a) where no new floorspace is created	£27
(b) up to 40 sq m of additional space	£27
(c) between 40 and 75 sq m additional space	£53
(d) for each additional 75 sq m	£53 to a maximum of £2650
Outline permission (depending on size of development)	£53 – to a maximum of £1325
Car parks, service roads or other accesses for existing use	£27
Change of use	£53

Applications and approval

There are four types of planning application.

1 An outline planning application This is largely to establish in principle whether development can take place or not. It avoids the submission of detailed drawings. Any drawings submitted are for illustrative purposes only. It is often useful to apply for permission in outline to establish the type of development the planners will allow before committing yourself to any costs. Items such as external appearance of buildings, access and landscaping may be reserved for subsequent approval. Outline permission is not relevant to a development proposal which does not involve the erection of a building.

2 An application for approval of reserved matters This type of application is used when an outline approval has already been granted, but consideration and approval was not given to the reserved matters such as external appearance and landscaping outlined above.

3 A full application This is the approach to be adopted if development requires approval or a change of use is required. A full application is needed if development has been carried out without approval. This will clarify whether the completed works will be permitted by the planning authority.

4 Renewal of temporary permission or relief from conditional permission This type of application is usually made to clarify or modify conditions imposed in a previous approval.

Decisions are usually taken by a planning committee which will consist of local councillors and council officers (employees); the committee will usually make a decision within eight weeks. In exceptional cases a decision may take longer than eight weeks, but the authority must inform you in writing of any delay. If the planning authority places conditions on the approval, these will have to be met before development work can begin.

There are three types of approval given to any planning application. These are:

1 a definite refusal
2 a definite approval
3 a conditional approval.

Most applications are approved. Occasionally plans are refused. If your application is turned down the planning authority must indicate the precise reasons for doing so. These may include effects on road safety, noise and damage to the local environment. However, in this eventuality an appeal can be made to the Secretary of State. The

Department of the Environment has produced a free booklet, *Planning Appeals – A Guide,* which is available free from:

The Department of the Environment
Planning Inspectorate
Tollgate House
Houlton Street
Bristol BS2 9DJ

Six months are allowed from the date of the decision in which to appeal. Appeals do not have to be expensive as they need not involve a Public Inquiry and can be undertaken in writing. It is always worth considering an appeal as about 30 percent of appeals are successful.

Planning permission is valid for five years from the date of approval so that you do not have to start development work immediately. If after five years you have not begun work you will have to reapply for permission, which may not automatically be granted. Remember that planning decisions are enforceable by law and although many authorities may condone an oversight, enforcement can lead to the demolition of buildings or removal of all unapproved works.

Building regulations

Building regulations are an important statutory requirement to be considered when undertaking the conversion or subdivision of property. Do not be tempted to undertake any works without prior approval. There are very few occasions on which building regulation approval is not needed if space is being subdivided. The building regulations are administered by the building control department of the local council. The basic aim of the regulations are to ensure that buildings are structurally capable of withstanding intended types of use. The local authority has powers to enforce you to 'make good' or remove any unapproved building work.

The need for approval

There are three broad occasions when it is necessary to consult the building control department.

1 Building works: Most forms of building work will require approval. Applications are required for the erection of internal partitioning, any structural alterations and the installation of toilets and other such fittings.

2 Change of use: Any change of use from one purpose group to another, even if no building work is involved, will require approval (see below for meaning of purpose group).

3 Previously exempt buildings: Regulations relating to the structural stability of a building will apply if the buildings were previously either wholly or partially exempt from building regulations. Buildings with exemptions could include educational establishments and agricultural premises.

If any building work is required at a conversion or subdivision, permission will be needed. This work may include major or minor reconstruction or refurbishment. In either case the safety of the building in the event of a fire as well as the structural stability of the building is important.

The building regulations divide different uses into 'purpose groups', the most relevant of which are 'office', 'shop', 'factory', 'assembly' and 'storage'. These are not the same as the town planning 'use classes' described earlier. Make sure any units which are to be developed in a building have approval for the users who will occupy them. If the building has not got the correct approval it will be necessary to apply for permission to change the use. If the development involves a change of use, applications have to be submitted to building control officers stating both the existing use and the proposed new use of a building. This sometimes proves a difficulty as the owner of a building will not always know the activities to be performed by future (currently unknown) tenants. In this case building control requires a guarantee that all future users of the units will be within the same purpose group. The system of building control changed in November 1985 and from that date a variety of qualified groups known as Approved Inspectors are able in theory at least to grant building regulation approval. However, as this new system will not become fully operational for several years, application should still be made to the local authority building control department. Where building works are involved it is necessary to submit detailed drawings. You will be well advised to engage an architect or surveyor for this purpose. Unlike town planning decisions, building regulations approval is the responsibility of professional officers, not elected councillors.

A decision must be given within five weeks of plans being submitted. If after five weeks a decision has not been made, approval is deemed to have been given, unless an extension to a maximum of eight weeks in total has been mutually agreed. Building control approval is valid for three years from the date of the approval. After that date a new application has to be submitted. Whilst it is unlikely that the new application will be refused, some upgrading of specifications may be necessary. Recent changes in building regulations in insulation and ventilation standards would, for example, have necessitated upgradings for plans submitted in the recent past.

Fire resistance and control

As well as testing for structural stability, building regulations are also very concerned with the effects of fire on buildings. These considerations are slightly different from fire certificates which will be discussed on page 43.

The main danger being guarded against by building regulations at any development is the spread of fire, either within or between buildings. The design must be capable of ensuring minimum periods of fire resistance to elements of the structure of a building. These 'elements' include beams, columns, floors, external walls, compartment walls, structures enclosing protected shafts, load-bearing walls and galleries, etc. (These requirements are additional to the Means of Escape legislation enforceable by the Fire Authority. See page 43.)

Minimum periods of fire resistance required for the structural elements of any building are determined by the height, floor area and cubic capacity of the building. Fire resistance requirements tend to increase with the size (floor area and height) of the building. A careful note should therefore be made of these details before contacting building control officers for assistance or approval.

Minimum periods of fire resistance for the structural elements of a property are usually much higher in older multi-storey buildings than in single-storey buildings. Subdivision of a multi-storey building involving a change of use may require considerable extra building work to meet approved standards. The fire resistance of items such as walls, floors, beams, pillars, stairways and doors will have to be improved so that they survive longer in the event of a fire or do not allow the fire to travel so quickly. The expense involved with cladding beams or' pillars, introducing fire-resistant doors or protecting stairways can be considerable. This has reduced the viability of some conversion or subdivision schemes at multi-storey developments.

Access to a fire escape is a second factor which may restrict the subdivision of a property. This problem is also more pertinent in older multi-storey buildings. Subdivision may not be allowed if the building control officer or Fire Authority think that occupants would not be able to reach a place of safety in the event of fire. Travel distance to a protected area and means of escape are examined for any new units created. A person must be able to reach a fire exit or a place of safety within a direct travel distance of 12 metres or a circuitous travel route of 18 metres. The rigidity with which travel distance requirements are imposed will depend on the type of building, whether it is single- or multi-storey, and its use. Travel distance requirements tend to be more rigidly imposed in multi-storey buildings.

If certain requirements of the building regulations cannot be met it may be possible to obtain a relaxation. This can allow the waiving of certain regulations. Whether a relaxation is given will depend on the merits of the building itself. The provision of adequate fire fighting equipment, adequate means of escape, early warning systems and sprinkler systems can sometimes lead to a relaxation of requirements relating to building regulations.

Building regulation charges

Building approval involves the preparation of drawings; details about appropriate sizes and styles are included on the application forms. Approval also costs money. Fees chargeable are broadly in relation to the cost of the development work involved. This is one of those cases where it pays not to exaggerate total costs! An indication of building regulation charges is given in Table 5.2. All extensions and alterations are subject to VAT at 15 percent. This must be included in the estimated costs.

Table 5.2 Examples of building regulation fees

70% of estimated cost	Plan fee	Inspection fee
Under £1000	£3	£9
£1000 and under £2000	£7	£21
£10,000 and under £12,000	£32	£96
£100,000 and under £140,000	£203	£609
£700,000 and under £1,000,000	£945	£2835

Environmental health

The environmental health department of the local authority is responsible for the health and physical welfare of the population. There are several areas of any small unit development which may concern them, these include:

1 dust, odours, and fumes emitted from the new units
2 grit and dust from boilers and industrial processes
3 noise created by new users, often a problem in or near residential areas.

Remember to consider these factors because the local planners will consult with their environmental health colleagues about them. It is always worth a telephone call to the environmental health department to discuss your proposals. They may suggest modifications or statutory requirements which will have to be accommodated at your conversion or subdivision. The sooner you know about these factors the easier it will be to accommodate them at your development.

Statutory undertakers

The Gas, Water and Electricity Boards and British Telecom should also be consulted at an early stage of any development. Their interests will vary but might include:

1 an assessment of existing mains facilities or services for new and additional users
2 an examination of the condition of the existing mains service: it is frequently an opportunity for them to replace old outdated services or equipment
3 an examination of effluent or pollution problems.

The Boards will also be pleased to discuss servicing new units within the development.

Fire officers

A fire certificate will be needed from the local fire officer, to confirm that fire precautions taken in the building have reached a standard acceptable to the fire officer. Certain smaller buildings do not require a certificate. Never leave the possibility in doubt!

Although the building may have an existing certificate, it may be necessary to revalidate it if certain works take place. These include:

1 the conversion or subdivision of an existing building to multiple use
2 any change in the use class as defined in the building regulations
3 a change in tenants which results in changes in their production processes or the materials they store.

All buildings which require a fire certificate will normally require a fire alarm system, fire fighting equipment and possibly an emergency lighting system. If in any doubt, contact the chief fire officer.

Health and safety executive and other relevant bodies

There are three other main Acts which will apply to any development. These are: The Health and Safety at Work Act 1974; The Offices, Shops and Railways Premises Act 1963; and the Factories Act 1961. There is some degree of overlap between each of these.

Basically they ensure that employees work in a safe and comfortable environment, not too hot or cold, nor too damp or noisy. Welfare, catering and toilet facilities must be kept clean and safe as far as is reasonably practical. Equipment must be properly guarded and maintained. Floors, steps, stairs, passages and gangways must be kept safe and free from obstruction. Periodic inspections by the Factory Inspectorate will keep a check on your activities.

Other specific legislation applies to certain types of activity. Restaurants and cafés must be approved by a food inspector, whilst licences are required from the local authority for a wide range of trades such as ice-cream manufacture and hairdressing.

Local support

Local support can be an important element of a successful development. It is local support as well as technical opinion which is important in the local government decision-making process.

Many developers have successfully courted local people in the development of their proposals. The local community will frequently be willing to support a scheme which reuses a building that might otherwise become derelict and vandalized, especially if it creates local job opportunities. The key to success is communication. This can take time and energy but it is worth it.

1 Talk to the local community, both residents and businesses.
2 Use the local press to gain support for the venture. The local 'free' press have proved very useful to many developers.
3 Hold public meetings to present the case and allow questions. Some of the audience may be your future tenants.
4 Discuss your proposals with local councillors. Tell them about the benefits for the local community of your scheme. It is vital to gain political support.

Several developers have found it useful to maintain a dialogue with the community as ideas develop and the project comes to fruition. In discussing proposals remember that the audience may not be technically informed.

1   Be precise and uncomplicated, do not use technical jargon.
2   Use drawings and sketches.
3   Do not be patronizing.
4   Do not exaggerate.
5   Above all, listen and take advice.

Key points

1   Make a list of all those who may be involved in the approval of the project.
2   Talk to all those involved in approving the development and sound out their views at the start.
3   Be adaptable and take advice.
4   Do not be put off by technicalities.
5   Ask for any relaxations possible.
6   If necessary consider an appeal against any unfavourable decisions.
7   Remember to get the support of the local community.

Chapter 6

Design, Layout and Construction

The interrelationship of design with other activities in the development process

All buildings are different in layout and potential for subdivision or conversion; a range of designs are possible at any property. Despite local characteristics which will influence each building, there are two key factors which will determine the broad design and construction parameters at any development. These are, firstly, the amount which can be spent on the project and, secondly, the types of units to be developed. The feasibility study (see Chapter 4) will provide financial guidelines on expenditure; market research (see Chapter 3) will provide details about the type of units the market requires, including specifications of the size of units, probable types of user, facilities required and necessity for business support services. These two factors will provide the information required to prepare an accurate guide to the type and cost of units to be designed and developed.

These details are usually gathered together into a single document called a 'development brief'. This provides guidelines for the design and development of a scheme which can be used by the developer or any professionals engaged in the project. The development brief will include a description of the project and an indication of the detailed elements of the scheme. It will specify, for example, the number and size of units, provide sketch plans of how these might be achieved, the amount to be spent, details of services required and general level of finishes. Some of these elements may have to be modified later because of financial considerations or as a result of discussions about rules and regulations. Because the design process does not take place in isolation from the processes of conforming to regulations (see Chapter 5) and obtaining finance (see Chapter 7) modifications are frequently required. Although inconvenient, the broad parameters of the development brief can easily be revised to accommodate such changes.

The design process itself will allow the costs estimated in the feasibility study (see Chapter 4) to be refined and estimated more accurately. A 'two-way' relationship will result. This should ensure that total costs are not exceeded and the overall profitability of a development (estimated in the feasibility study) is maintained.

If demand for larger sized units is buoyant in the local market, design and construction costs may be reduced or in some cases avoided altogether because little construction work will be required. For smaller sized units developers need to decide more carefully how to subdivide premises. The majority of developers converting property make a once and for all decision on the layout of the property, although some flexibility may be built into this decision.

Developers subdividing often make plans to refurbish their current area of underused space and then draw up contingency plans for further contraction if their business continues to require less space. Although gradual contraction will require a greater total movement of machinery over time, it does allow companies to enter the property market progressively. This places fewer demands on company cashflow. It also allows companies to learn from experience how best to develop the remaining areas of their property.

There are major disadvantages in developing a site piecemeal in spite of its initial attraction of linking development to cashflow. Firstly, by developing a site gradually the first tenants will take all the prime sites or areas, leaving units of an inconvenient shape or size which are more difficult to let. Secondly, because most tenants want space immediately they will not consider unfinished units. Prospective tenants also find it difficult to imagine what a 1000 or 2000 square foot unit will look like in the corner of an office complex or factory. Thirdly, it is probable that, as tenants are fitted into remaining units, incompatible users may be located next to each other; retailers may end up next to noxious chemical processors and offices may be located next to noisy metal engineers. Finally, the cost of developing units incrementally is more difficult to calculate in advance, making feasibility assessment more difficult with the possible effect of developments exceeding their budgets, thus leading to an uneconomic development.

Design

The development brief will provide a valuable guide to the types of units which should be constructed and the amount of money available to undertake a development. The brief will contain details of the following features:

1 Construction/layout guidelines
   a Size of units required.
   b Types of user; this will provide information about items such as: noise considerations, access requirements, car parking considerations and office display requirements.
   c Facilities required such as: toilets, telephones, three-phase electricity, gas, extra lighting and strengthened floors.
   d Business services; the amount and type of central services required such as: reception, display area, telephone answering, typing facilities, photocopying, telex and facsimile.
2 Financial guidelines – these will usually be given as maximum costs or percentages for the following items:
   a Professional fees (designer, architect, planner, financial consultants, etc.).

b   Building costs (site works, roof, windows, doors, walls, etc.).

c   Installation costs (electricity, heating, ventilation, lighting, gas, etc.).

d   Interest on finance borrowed, contingencies (usually 10–15 percent of total costs included for an error in financial estimates).

The development brief will provide an accurate guide to any designer of the cost constraints, types of unit required and other associated conditions to be taken into consideration during the design process. The designer will then use these guidelines to incorporate all the elements into plans for the development of the building.

At many smaller developments, in companies with expertise in design or at developments requiring little construction work, consultation with professional designers will be unnecessary. All that may be required in these cases is an architect (or other professional) to prepare drawings of the proposed development for eventual planning and building regulation approval, and a builder or quantity surveyor to estimate costs. This will ensure costs are still within feasibility study guidelines. Builders will generally provide free estimates. Quantity surveyors will charge for their services on the basis of a percentage of development costs (usually between 2 and 5 percent). Estimates are important even if you intend to use your own personnel. You will still need accurate assessment of quantities and costs.

At larger developments where a considerable amount of design work is involved it is advisable to engage a project architect. Their fees will vary but can be based on a fixed sum, an hourly rate or a percentage (usually between 8 and 12 percent) of total development costs. Before employing an architect ask to see some of their previous work. Try to ensure that they have some experience in industrial and commercial buildings and/or refurbishment. Some practices specialize in conversion and workspace schemes and are aware of the needs and problems of small businesses and small business units. Local colleges and universities can also help in the design process. Many educational institutions are keen to give their students real world projects to design. Academic institutions are also very keen to be seen to be helping the local community wherever possible. The design of a conversion or subdivision project could therefore be undertaken at very low cost, or in some cases no cost at all, by students as project work during part of their architecture or design course.

Whether you are designing a conversion or subdivision yourself or using other groups it is worth visiting other projects to see what approach they have taken to design and layout. You can often pick up many important cost- or time-saving ideas. It is always important to discuss the design with tenants as well as the developer. It is the tenant who experiences the good and bad points of the scheme. Human nature being what it is, tenants tend to emphasize the bad points – landlords the good. Both will give you an excellent picture of the scheme.

The development brief and consultation process outlined so far in this chapter will provide a guide to the general design concepts which will be adopted in developing a site. These design concepts are used in designing and planning two areas of development activity: site layout and building layout. Both these activities require careful design and planning at any development. They have been separated in this book so that the general principles involved in each process can be reviewed more clearly.

Site and building layout: an introduction

Planning and design is nearly always undertaken for unknown tenants. Market research will give a good indication of the type of tenants to expect but their individual requirements will not be known until later in the development process. Despite, and in many ways because of, these problems, it is important to design a layout for the types of business your market research has shown are likely to occupy the development. It is impossible to give individual details for every type of building or style of development; instead a number of basic guidelines will be recommended concerning the layout of any conversion or subdivision. These have been divided into two sections: site layout – access and circulation at the site, and building layout – the design and construction work required within a building to provide small business units.

Site layout

Access to the site

Conversion or subdivision will frequently intensify the use of a site and increase the pressures associated with traffic movement at the site or on surrounding roads. Site access is an issue which the local planning authority will investigate if planning permission is required. They will investigate how safely traffic can leave your site and move onto main roads. To overcome these problems it may be necessary to build new entrances, reorganize the use of exterior space and possibly even demolish buildings. Consider these problems carefully and try to clarify what the main difficulties will be. Do not be afraid to approach your local authority's planning or building control departments to ask for advice about how you might overcome these problems. There are few local authorities which would not send a member of their staff to your site to discuss your problems and proposals.

Ease of movement within a site is also important. This will include both cars and large delivery lorries. Planning authorities will not usually allow vehicles to reverse from a site onto main roads. For this reason a layout which allows traffic to circulate easily is advantageous. At many sites routes for traffic to circulate have already been established. At some sites it may only be possible to provide adequate circulation by demolishing some buildings.

Car parking

Although most properties will already have some car parking spaces, many planning authorities expect developers to provide additional car parking space if needed to bring a conversion or subdivision scheme up to current standards. This can be particularly difficult where site densities are high and suitable areas for car parking space may be limited. At these developments selective demolition may be necessary to provide these additional spaces. Because each industry has different employment densities, car parking requirements vary between industries. The interpretation of suitable car parking standards also varies between local authorities. Table 6.1 shows the average car parking requirements of local authorities in England. These figures are a guide to estimate how much car parking space will be required at your development; the local authority planning department will clarify their exact requirements.

Table 6.1   Average car parking requirements of local authorities in England

Type of business	Floorspace for which one car parking space is required (sq ft)
Retail	640
Office	425
Industry	575
Warehousing	2400

Building layout and design

The layout and design of every building is unique because each building's characteristics will determine its development potential. Broad development guidelines will be determined by the development brief, but building layout should also be considered in relation to site layout discussed in the previous section. Careful design of the access to the building or individual units can help to overcome site layout problems. Also included in this section are details of business services, heating and lighting and the level of decoration which will have to be considered when designing units within the building.

Using the natural assets of a building

Maximum use should be made of all the natural assets of a building. Wherever possible existing entrances, walls, windows, lifts (in multi-storey premises) and services, including toilets, should be retained. To remove or replace them costs money. In general the most cost-effective developments are those which keep replacement and construction costs to a minimum. Multi-storey buildings with single tenants occupying each floor provide the best example of a scheme which is 'ready made' requiring no construction costs.

The creation of units of a similar size or type at a site can lead to considerable problems if that sector of the market suddenly collapses. Indeed, market research is unlikely to show that a single size or type of unit should be built at a development; this research will usually suggest a range or variety of units which are in demand. Try to diversify a development as much as possible within the constraints of market research information. The old adage of not putting all your eggs in one basket is particularly appropriate.

Walls and partitions

When constructing walls or partitions it is necessary to consider two features: flexibility and insulation. Flexibility will allow you to expand or contract the size of units as required. To gain flexibility you will normally have to 'trade off' some of the insulation qualities of a partition. This includes insulation in terms of both noise and heat. Moveable partitions allowing flexibility are usually poor insulators, whereas breeze-block or brick-built walls are good insulators but restrict flexibility. One way of overcoming these problems and building in flexibility is to divide the property into different sections or areas by making the maximum use of existing solid walls, or the positioning of newly constructed brick or breeze-block walls. Some developers have created individual areas within a property which can be further subdivided by flexible partitions. In this way compatible tenants can be located in the same area. Buildings are thus 'zoned' for different uses. Tenants in these areas will be either compatible or tolerant of each other's mutually conflicting activities. Units within these 'zoned' areas can then be constructed by using more flexible partitions.

Flexibility can also allow the size of individual units to be modified virtually on request. Empty floorspace adjacent to an expanding tenant could be utilized if partitions are removed. Expansion is usually relatively easy if space is available; contraction in size may be more of a problem. The area remaining after contraction may not be required by surrounding tenants or it may be unsuitable for the development of a new unit. In either of these cases partitions may have been installed but their advantages may not always be realized. As a result flexibility should never become an overriding goal at any development. Flexibility can be beneficial, particularly when accommodating tenants at a newly completed site, but its benefits cannot always be realized. Various methods, materials and costs for partitions are given in Table 6.2.

Table 6.2 Costs of raw materials used in the construction of 12 ft by 8 ft partition (November 1985 prices)

Type of partition	Cost of materials
Purpose-made (high insulation qualities)	£87.30
Purpose-made (average insulation quality)	£58.39
Brick	£46.00
Breeze-block	£36.90
Plaster-board on a wooden frame	£18.80

In order to gain flexibility, developers usually have to 'trade off' some of the insulation qualities or pay considerably more in the cost of raw materials. The most flexible partitions are composed of plaster-board on a wooden frame. If carefully handled they are reusable but they have poor insulation qualities. Plaster-board can also be easily damaged, particularly in an industrial environment. Although leases may include a 'full repair clause' (requiring the repair of all damage to a unit, see Chapter 9) the implementation of such a clause can be a source of conflict between the landlord and tenant if the partitions are not adequate. This can result in tenants leaving their premises for alternative accommodation.

More sturdy and better insulated methods of construction are breeze-block or brick walls. For the most part these are normally totally inflexible. The provision of a large door in this type of wall can provide all the access required to a neighbouring unit allowing the two to be combined to provide a single, larger unit.

The only type of partition which allows both flexibility and insulation are purpose-made plaster-boards with foam coverings. These are easy to put up and allow flexibility but they are relatively expensive and can be easily damaged.

If partitions are constructed they do not always provide a complete barrier from the floor to the ceiling, although this may be required for insulation purposes. In the majority of cases a partition of only 8 feet in height will meet all statutory requirements. Your architect or local authority building control department will be able to advise you on local circumstances. Considerable savings can be made by constructing partitions only to a height of 8 feet although problems of security may arise. The emission of dust, fumes and noise to other units or communal corridors or reception areas may also be a problem.

Access to units and the provision of corridors

Wherever possible provide external access doors at ground level to each unit. This is beneficial for individual tenants and also for fire regulations (see Chapter 5). At some multi-storey buildings built on a slope it is possible to provide 'ground-floor' access to different levels where upper floors are adjacent to the slope. Many multi-storey buildings possess goods lifts. If these are in good working order, upper-storey units should have a layout which allows as many tenants as possible to make use of the lift.

If a site or building is next to a main road, locate retailers or office-oriented tenants at ground level with access directly onto the road so that they can attract passing trade. This also ensures that their customers are not wandering through a development and causing inconvenience to other tenants. If direct access for customers to retailers or office tenants is not possible, locate their units as near as possible to the main entrance. This should reduce traffic flow and inconvenience through the remainder of the development.

Companies using large amounts of raw materials, heavy goods or machinery should, wherever possible, be placed at ground level or adjacent to heavy goods lifts. This will reduce their problems in getting goods in and out of their unit. At most sites ground-floor units will have the greatest floor-loading capacity; as a result they are able to withstand the weight and attrition of heavy machinery. Tenants with lighter machinery or those using fewer raw materials are usually best suited to upper floors at multi-storey developments. Office or craft uses will be suited to upper storeys.

At many multi-storey developments or large single-storey sites it will be necessary to provide corridors for access to individual units. Wherever possible corridor space should be kept to a minimum, whilst conforming to the statutory standards imposed by fire regulations. Because corridors are communal space they are not paid for directly by tenants. They are in effect, therefore, space provided by a developer on which no return is obtained. More importantly, in many cases they also provide a fire escape route from a unit. Consultation with building officers will clarify details about fire regulations. In general two escape routes from a unit are required. As Figure 6.1 shows, these can either be provided by a corridor, which is costly to install and maintain, or maximum use can be made of all the floorspace by providing fire escape doors into adjacent units. The use of these types of doors should not be overlooked because they can provide considerable savings. If tenants are worried about theft of their equipment from adjacent tenants sharing a fire door, the doors can be connected to an alarm system. Fire doors will usually have to be fire resistant for periods of 30 minutes or longer to impede the spread of fire at a building. Once again, consultation with the local authority building control department will clarify the position.

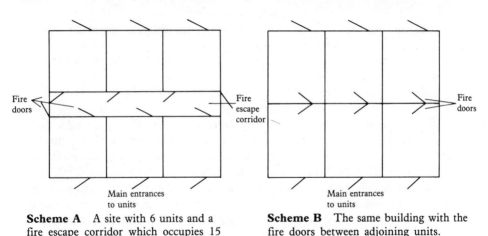

Scheme A A site with 6 units and a fire escape corridor which occupies 15 percent of the floorspace.

Scheme B The same building with the fire doors between adjoining units.

Figure 6.1 Providing fire escape through adjacent units

Toilet and washing facilities

Most industrial tenants are usually willing to share toilet and washing facilities with other tenants. Office groups and retailers, particularly those handling food, often require their own facilities. If you cannot develop a property to provide individual access to toilets it may be necessary to construct new toilet facilities. This can be expensive depending on the amount of building involved. One way around this problem is to provide portable toilet and washing facilities (portaloos). These usually require less plumbing and they can be bought as items of capital equipment. This means you can gain an allowance for their purchase against corporation tax (50 percent of their value until April 1986 and decreasing to 25 percent of their value thereafter).

Business services

The exact nature of the business services provided will be governed by market research. There are various ways and methods in which these can be provided. The positioning of communal business services can be important. They can either be placed in a central position to allow easier access for tenants or at the entrance. Preference is usually for a position by the entrance, so that whoever is administering them can act as a receptionist and security guard to prevent the entrance of casual visitors. If a communal sales unit is developed it is usually best to locate this next to the main entrance with a reception and business service section beyond (further away from the entrance). This has two major advantages: casual visitors can still be prevented from entering the area occupied by tenants, and all visitors and prospective tenants will gain a favourable impression of the range of activities and level of production within the development.

Signposting and visitors

One problem which occurs at most developments is the difficulty customers, suppliers and visitors have in finding particular units. Tenants and receptionists will know exactly where each business is located, but to the majority of visitors the site may seem like a very confusing rabbit warren. Good signposting is essential. It is usually impossible to give directions for every single unit, particularly at larger sites. As a result, some developers have adopted a colour (number or letter) coding system. Individual areas of the development containing a number of units, or each floor at multi-storey properties, are given a colour (number or letter). Throughout the development, signs can direct visitors to these colour-coded areas and within these areas more specific signs to individual units can be erected. The success of this system is reliant on visitors being aware of how the system operates. Full details of which companies are within each area and how the system works should be clearly visible at each entrance. If possible, attach these details to every signpost and have copies available for tenants to distribute to their customers and visitors.

A simple but very effective method of signposting individual units was developed by Tony Devernold, a tenant at Otley Mills near Leeds (see the case study in Chapter 10). Essentially an ordinary fluorescent strip light is encased by a wooden box which displays the tenant's name (see Figure 6.2). At Otley Mills the signposts are used internally, but the system could easily be adapted for outdoor use by using weatherproof fittings. Apart from being simple and efficient, the system has a number of other advantages. The sign can be easily constructed and painted to conform to any colour (or other) coding system within a development (signs in red in one area and blue and another, for example). If linked to the tenants' electricity supply, this system not only acts as an 'open'/'closed' board but ensures lights are not left on at night. In communal corridors the light from just a few of these signs is sufficient to light the corridor. As a result, lighting provided by the developers in corridors is reduced to a minimum. Since many developers complain of communal lights being left on throughout the night, this can be beneficial.

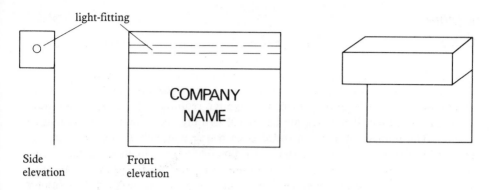

light-fitting

COMPANY
NAME

Side
elevation

Front
elevation

Figure 6.2   Signposting for individual units used at Otley Mills

Heating

Three approaches can be taken when providing heating. These are:

1 fully heated units
2 background heating to protect water pipes and sprinklers against freezing
3 no heating provided.

It is often advisable not to provide heating at a conversion or subdivision. Many developers have had considerable problems trying to resolve arguments between tenants about how much heat they have used. These disputes have been most frequent amongst industrial tenants who do not require heating because of the nature of their business: glass blowers and cooked-food manufacturers provide an example. As a result, many developers have required all tenants to provide their own heating. Amongst industrial users whose heating requirements vary this is acceptable, but many retailers and office businesses expect heating to be provided in their premises. Because these groups all require heating at a similar level they are usually more willing to share costs on the basis of floorspace occupied. But even amongst these businesses problems about heating sometimes occur. If you do provide heating, ensure there is a clause in the lease that apportions these costs amongst the tenants which receive this service.

At some developments with large amounts of exposed water pipes or a sprinkler system it is beneficial to have a background heating system which will prevent these pipes freezing. During winter, particularly at Christmas when your tenants are not heating their premises, an additional heating system connected to a 'froststat' (a thermostatic system which turns heating on when a temperature of about 36°F or less is reached) can be essential. One way to prevent this problem is to lag all water pipes thoroughly, but during the coldest winters lagging can be insufficient. An alternative method which has been used to protect some sprinkler systems during winter has been to drain water from the system and replace it with compressed air. If the sprinkler is then activated the compressed air is quickly expelled and water follows from the main supply in a matter of seconds.

Lighting

Lighting is another area where a range of provision is possible. Lighting in communal areas is always required but within units provision can vary from a high quality system to none at all. Most developers provide a minimum level of lighting using fluorescent lights on chains. This is usually sufficient to illuminate most units and allows tenants limited flexibility in organizing their own lighting requirements. Tenants can lower the fluorescent tubes if they require additional lighting over a particular machine or activity. The number of lights provided at each unit is usually decided by trial and error. With the help of a few colleagues it is possible to hang lights temporarily from the ceiling. These can then be rearranged until they illuminate the unit sufficiently and, when a suitable arrangement has been found, permanently installed. If additional lighting is required, this can be installed by the tenant. Some groups, particularly retailers and office activities, may require additional lighting. It is usually best to allow them to install extra lighting themselves. A period of reduced rents may be necessary but in most cases their needs will be relatively specialized and beyond the limits of what a landlord could reasonably be expected to provide.

Decoration

The quality of decoration within a unit can be important to the attraction of tenants. The level of decoration required will primarily relate to your market research. In general it is best not to overprovide. It is far easier to raise standards, if demand requires better quality units, than it is to lower them. Higher levels of decoration increase construction costs and raise the rental levels required to provide a viable return at a development. Most tenants do not expect a very high level of decoration. If required, it is possible to offer periods of reduced rents at the beginning of a tenancy to allow them to redecorate or refurbish the unit to their own requirements.

Consultation with officials

At all stages of the design process it is essential to consult building officers and planning officials from the local authority. It was noted in the previous chapter that they are usually willing to undertake site visits and offer advice. Even at the very early stages of a development it is worth contacting the industrial development officer from the local authority. They are usually keen to assist any project which will assist the growth of local small business. They will often give you a formal introduction to their colleagues in the planning and building control department and this may help to ease the passage of your planning applications or help to overcome problems at later stages.

Construction

When the layout and design have been finalized and approved by the appropriate groups construction work can begin. You should, though, give thought to the way you will undertake the construction work well in advance. If an architect is undertaking all design and development work, he will administer and contract all building and constructional activities. If you are organizing this work, you will have to consult the craftsmen, builders, gas and electricity personnel included in the following section.

Construction work can be undertaken at varying degrees of cost, quality and speed. There are a number of different approaches which can be taken.

Your own workforce   Look around your own workforce. Frequently you will find people who are adequately trained or experienced in building, construction or advanced DIY. They can undertake much of the work themselves. Where particular skills are not available, such as bricklaying, they can be brought in. Similarly, specialized equipment, mixers, diggers and the like can be hired when needed.

Frequently developers have used their own workers when the main business has been slack so that, rather than laying off workers, they can be retained. In this way there is minimum disruption to the company's main activities. As you are paying only one set of overheads, costs can be reduced. Consult your workers about this approach during the planning stage of your subdivision.

Although the cost of using your own workers may be very low and you can control their speed of work, remember that the quality of their work has to meet the building inspector's approval.

Self-employed builders   Self-employed builders will often undertake conversion and subdivision work far more cheaply than jobbing or contract builders. They are also more willing to come and undertake one-off jobs if the developer's own personnel lack certain skills. Self-employed builders are relatively cheap. At present bricklayers, joiners and general construction workers can cost as little as £5 per hour but costs will vary throughout the UK. Builders are usually best found by the recommendation of friends or colleagues with experience of their work and its quality. In general they can often provide good quality work relatively cheaply. One problem with individual self-employed builders is their speed; on smaller jobs they are quicker than most but on larger jobs they will lack the manpower and resources to complete work at a faster rate. If the manager with some building or DIY skills is appointed at an early stage in a development, he can manage a number of self-employed tradesmen and the problem of the speed associated with hiring single workers can be overcome by employing a variety of different groups at the same time. The work of self-employed builders may not always be insured. Self-employed builders and jobbing and contract builders who are members of the National Register of Warranted Builders or Builders Employers Confederation can offer a more fully insured service. For 1 percent of the contract cost of any building works, up to two years' guarantee can be given on the quality of work completed.

Jobbing and contract builders   The use of jobbing and contract builders to complete a development will usually cost far more than the other two alternatives. It does mean you have less involvement in the construction process and it can, although not always, be less troublesome. Always obtain three or four estimates. Get at least one from an area away from the development. Estimates often depend on how much a builder needs the work. Rates and quotations can vary enormously for exactly the same work.

Some developers, in no hurry to complete a development, have persuaded building company managers to send along their workers, at a reduced rate, when they have no other work. This can greatly reduce costs.

The speed and quality of jobbing and contract builders' work is usually good and can be assured by writing a clause into their contract which stipulates that all work must be completed by a certain date.

The developer will have to decide his own priorities with regard to cost, quality and speed of work. Whichever construction method is used, the building inspector will visit the development regularly to ensure that all work is undertaken to a high enough standard to pass all statutory regulations. Unfortunately, since the introduction of charges for building control, a site visit fee is now payable for each visit. Examples of inspection fees are given in Table 5.2 (p.43).

Electricity and gas

In many buildings suitable for conversion or subdivision the gas and electricity system will have been designed and installed to meet the requirements of only one user, not the variety or number of tenants that will eventually inhabit your development. For this reason considerable rewiring and rerouting of gas and electricity is often required. In many older premises rewiring is frequently necessary anyway because of the deterioration of the existing system. These costs can be considerable. Make sure they are carefully estimated during the feasibility study. Where appropriate, reuse as much of the existing wiring system as possible. Frequently it is very difficult to trace wiring. It can be useful to track down the electrician who installed or serviced the supply. If you can re-employ them or persuade them to talk to your electrician, it may be possible to reuse more of the existing system.

Estimating the costs of gas and electricity installation or refurbishing an existing system can be very difficult. It is an area where costs can escalate very easily as faults and difficulties arise when work is in progress. It is useful to get a quotation for the work from an experienced electrician or fitter even if your own personnel are undertaking the work.

It is possible to undertake a conversion or subdivision and simply allow tenants to use existing gas and electricity supplies. A contribution to bills can then be made by each tenant. This frequently leads to problems and arguments about how much each tenant has used. To prevent these difficulties it is far easier to install separate gas and electricity meters. This need not be expensive.

Electricity   There are two common types of electrical supply for industrial users: single-phase and three-phase. The single-phase system is used in most domestic applications. In simple terms, three-phase is a heavy duty supply suitable for businesses using large amounts of electricity. The system provides three positive wires instead of the one supplied by single-phase. Most developers have found that single-phase is suitable for most tenants. As a result they install a single-phase supply to all units. If tenants require three-phase electricity this is provided to junction boxes at various parts of a development so that it can be installed to their unit relatively easily. The additional costs are usually passed on to the tenant.

All separate electricity supplies have to be installed by the Electricity Board. The cost of installing a separate electricity supply and meter will vary depending upon how much excavation work is required. The standard price is about £150. But, like gas, this will vary depending upon how much work is required to fit a new supply. A separate supply ensures that tenants are charged directly for all electricity they use.

A sub-meter can be purchased from the Electricity Board and this can be fitted by your own personnel. The usual price for a sub-meter is about £80. You, as the landlord, will be charged for all the electricity used at the site but you have an indisputable record of how much each tenant has consumed and you can apportion costs accordingly. It is well worth writing such an agreement into any leases.

Your local Electricity Board will give you further information. They usually send someone to discuss your needs and probable costs.

Gas Gas may not be required or available at all developments, but if it is, the Gas Board insist on fitting all new meters. The cost of laying a new gas supply pipeline and installing a separate meter will vary depending upon how much digging work has to be done to access the main supply. The average cost for installing a meter, digging about 70 feet to the nearest mains supply and fitting a non-return valve is about £400. With a separate supply the tenant will be charged directly by the Gas Board.

A cheaper alternative is to fit a sub-meter to your existing supply at the nearest point to each new unit. The cost of a domestic sub-meter (212 mm supply pipe), which will usually be good enough to most units, is about £60. An industrial sub-meter (550 mm supply pipe) is about £150. Fitting will usually cost about £75. With a sub-metered supply you will be charged for all gas supplied to the development but you will have an indisputable record of how much a tenant has used. You can then charge them for all the gas they have consumed; it is worth writing this stipulation into a lease.

Your local Gas Board will give you further information. They will usually send an engineer to your property to discuss your particular needs and likely costs.

Several different approaches can be taken when supplying gas or electricity to a unit. Some developers simply supply services to a junction box, allowing tenants to install their own power sockets or gas points throughout the unit. Other developers have provided these fittings throughout the unit before tenants occupy units. The approach which should be taken depends upon the 'standard' of the conversion and the financial resources available.

With both gas and electricity it is essential to remember that the development of new units and the arrival of tenants may well increase the consumption of gas and electricity at a site. In some cases, this may necessitate the installation of pipes and wires which give an increased supply at a development. This can be costly so it is essential to consult Gas and Electricity Boards about probable future requirements.

Reducing rates during conversion

Whilst conversion work is in progress it is possible to reduce the rates charged on the premises. If during conversion or subdivision the building cannot be used for its normal purpose, the Inland Revenue valuation officers have the power to levy a nominal £1 rate until the conversion or subdivision process is completed. For further details contact your local Inland Revenue valuation officer.

Key points

1 Prepare a development brief.
2 Throughout the design process ensure costs correspond with previous estimates.
3 The site layout should allow adequate access, circulation and car parking.
4 The building layout should compliment and help to overcome site layout problems.
5 Use the natural assets of a building to reduce construction costs.
6 Within the building separate incompatible users.
7 Decide on the levels of heating, lighting and decoration to be provided.
8 Where necessary consult the relevant planning, building and other officials throughout the design process.
9 Decide which type of builders will construct the development.
10 Consult Electricity and Gas Boards at an early stage to assess future requirements.
11 Apply for a rating reduction if the building cannot be used for its normal purpose during construction work.

Chapter 7

Finance and Funding

Most conversion and subdivision schemes require some level of borrowing to turn the developer's ideas into reality. The financial position of a company or organization will always determine its borrowing requirements. At some subdivisions a small loan may be all that is required to purchase materials and get a scheme started. Conversions frequently require considerably more external funding to assist with both the purchase and conversion of the property. Some companies with surplus financial resources may not require any assistance. Others make use of company pension funds for the purchase and conversion of property.

Financial considerations will arise during the process of undertaking feasibility studies (see Chapter 4) and designing a scheme (see Chapter 6). The design, feasibility and finance processes are closely interwoven and the three tend to proceed simultaneously. Financial organizations will not lend without some idea of your project and its feasibility. If they are prepared to lend less than you require, you will either have to redesign the project and revise the feasibility studies to meet their proposed level of funding or approach other financial organizations. Your accountant will play a key role in determining your borrowing requirements and negotiating with financial organizations. The organizations to approach and the usual process of negotiations are outlined in the first part of this chapter.

Although most firms needing finance will have to borrow some money from a commercial lender, several sources of grants and preferential loans (at favourable rates) are also available for conversion and subdivision schemes. Some are directed exclusively at small businesses, some are only available for local authorities or charitable organizations, others are available to all groups. Further details of these are given toward the end of this chapter. In addition to financial assistance, some groups can also apply for manpower resources under the community programme.

Sources of finance

Deciding which financial source to approach depends primarily on the amount you want to borrow. The list below describes some of the most commonly used sources of finance. High Street banks, building societies, local authorities and the Council for Small Industries in Rural Areas (CoSIRA) are the best sources for smaller loans. With the exception of local authorities, all of the sources below are willing to lend to the larger borrower under the right circumstances.

High Street banks

The High Street banks are the most obvious source of loans. Any local branch should be able to provide further details and itemize the information they will require from you before finance will be granted. If you do use them, always contact more than one because their interest rates and terms vary. In recent years the commercial banks have become much more flexible and positive in their lending policies to small businesses (thanks in part to a government loan guarantee scheme). They used to lend only relatively modest amounts to small businesses and usually over time periods of less than five years. Now they are increasingly competitive, and under the right circumstances most banks are prepared to lend for up to twenty years. They will consider lending almost any sum of money provided that suitable security is available.

Building societies

Some building societies, predominantly the smaller ones, give mortgages to purchase industrial and commercial property. Indeed, many societies are keen to expand their lending in this direction; this may be one area of building society activity which grows in future. Some of the larger societies offer private purpose loans which, as their name suggests, can be used for any purpose including the purchase of premises for conversion or subdivision work. The type of security required is variable, but if a large enough proportion of your household mortgage is paid off, this may satisfy their requirements.

Local authority schemes

Many local authorities, anxious to encourage local economic development and employment growth, offer loans and in some cases grants to help small businesses purchase, convert or subdivide premises. As the availability and terms of these grants and loans varies between authorities, contact your local authority's industrial or economic development officer for information.

Council for Small Industries in Rural Areas

The Council for Small Industries in Rural Areas (CoSIRA) aims to improve the prosperity of small businesses in rural areas in England. Similar services are provided by the small business divisions of the Scottish and Welsh Development Agencies (addresses in Appendix 1). Loans for the acquisition (both freehold and long lease), improvement, adaption or extension of buildings are available to small firms in the manufacturing, service and tourism sectors in English rural areas and county towns with no more than 10,000 inhabitants. Building loans are up to 20 years in duration and range from a minimum of £750 to a maximum of £75,000. For further details contact the local CoSIRA offices; addresses are given in Appendix 4.

Merchant banks

Merchant banks provide long-term finance and capital for small businesses. The majority of their business is with term loans and mortgages of between 5 and 25 years. With adequate security there is no real limit to the amount they will lend, but their minimum is usually around £20,000. They are really only an appropriate financial source for the purchase of and refurbishment work at conversion schemes or very large subdivisions. Because of the larger amounts they deal with, merchant banks tend to lend only to companies or individuals with a proven track record. They usually insist on a thorough look through a business's previous trading accounts. Your track record will determine how flexible the merchant banks will be. They will usually lend up to 75–80 percent of the purchase price of a property's value. One drawback of many merchant banks is that they often lend only on an equity basis, by taking shares in your company, in return for the capital they loan.

Investors in Industry PLC

Investors in Industry (previously known as ICFC) is a merchant bank type of organization owned by a consortium of the High Street banks and the Bank of England. The address of its head office is given in Appendix 1. Its particular interest, as its name suggests, is with industrial lending. Investors in Industry prides itself on its assistance to small private companies. In 1985 two-thirds (£227m) of its new investment went to small businesses and over half of the year's total investments were in amounts of £100,000 or less. Loan duration is normally from 7 to 20 years. Its emphasis on lending to smaller industrial companies can sometimes make it more responsive than merchant banks who have a much wider ranging investment policy.

Discussion with your accountant will resolve how much your company or organization will need to borrow. They may also be able to suggest other sources of finance more applicable to your particular requirements. Readers requiring more detail about finance and financial resources should consult a specialist text on the subject. A particularly useful example is Clive Woodcock's *Raising Finance: The Guardian Guide for the Small Business* published by Kogan Page.

Negotiating with financial organizations

Although there are numerous sources of finance, the procedures adopted when trying to arrange finance are broadly similar. Precise details will vary according to the nature of your conversion or subdivision scheme, the sum required and the organization you approach. The procedures set out below are those which commonly apply when borrowing sums of between £5000 and £50,000. If you are seeking a smaller amount, the procedures may be shorter. If you wish to borrow more, you may have to prepare more detailed information.

At an early stage in your decision to convert or subdivide a property you should make an initial visit to the financial organizations you hope to use. An early visit will familiarize you with their lending policies so that you can decide which will be most appropriate for your requirements. This initial visit also alerts them to the fact that, unless they reject your ideas at the outset, you intend to return when your subdivision plans are more advanced or when a property for conversion has been found.

When plans are sufficiently advanced and you have produced a draft layout and associated feasibility study for the proposed conversion or subdivision, arrange a second visit to the financial organizations. You should prepare a brief document (three or four pages) giving basic information about your conversion or subdivision scheme. This should include details about your business, the property to be developed, the proposed layout and costs of the development, the amount you wish to borrow and the preferred method of repayment. It will also be useful to have a written letter of recommendation from your accountant, a professional business adviser or, if appropriate, from your bank manager. At this meeting you will be sounded out in a fairly general way. It is unlikely that you will be asked any highly specific or penetrating questions about your company's financial or cashflow position, precise costs of each element of the development, or exact rental income, but be ready with some basic facts and figures just in case. If they are satisfied with your initial ideas and interested in your proposition they will invite you back to another interview for a more thorough assessment. You will need to prepare a much more detailed document of your proposals and requirements for this meeting. Because of its essentially financial nature this is best prepared with an accountant. It should include the following information:

1 Details of your business (your product, markets etc.) together with any sales or publicity material.
2 Details of the property to be developed (or purchased in the case of a conversion).
3 Details about the development, number of units to be created and costs.
4 Market research information (see Chapter 3), probable rental levels and expected annual rental income.
5 Complete details of the feasibility study (see Chapter 4).
6 The amount of finance you require and the preferred methods of borrowing and repayment.
7 An historical analysis of your firm's finances (generally three years minimum).
8 The most recent trading figures and audited accounts.
9 A forecast of your cashflow and future trading position.
10 Details (if appropriate) of your management team and their expertise.
11 Your company's major shareholders (if any).
12 Your current banking arrangements.

Preparing a document of this nature takes time. Most of the details about your conversion or subdivision can be gained from your market research (see Chapter 3), design appraisal (see Chapter 6) and feasibility study (see Chapter 4). More general details about your company (or organization) and its trading position will have to be obtained from a variety of other sources. If you are confident about your development and believe you can put forward a strong case for financial support, you can prepare this document before your second visit to a financial organization.

Preparing the document so far in advance can be a gamble, especially if it later becomes clear that they are not interested in your proposal. But most financial organizations will be impressed by your having prepared such a professional document in advance and without them having to specify exactly what is required. It will certainly enhance their estimation of your management capabilities.

During the final meeting you will be asked questions about the accuracy and realism of your development proposals and forecasts. If your knowledge of accounts is not strong enough to withstand a barrage of questions in this area, take your accountant with you. This should ensure a professional presentation. It does not mean that you can sit back and leave everything to your accountant. You too will need to know the document inside out. Be confident and positive. Their personal impressions are very important. All things being equal, it is often a 'gut feeling' about the applicant which sways the final decision. Experience, integrity, imagination, logic and good health are the key attributes that most investment managers will be looking for in a client.

A word of caution is appropriate here. Most lending agencies can differentiate between an accountant's plan and a prospective developer's plan. They will be looking for what you want to do, aided by your financial advisers, not what your advisers would like you to do. After all, it is you as the developer who will be controlling the conversion or subdivision scheme.

Either during or soon after this meeting you will be told whether money will be made available to you. If you do not succeed with one organization take heart – there are plenty more you can approach. Try to learn the lessons of your failure so that you can prepare a stronger case next time. However, if you get a series of rejections you may need to rethink your proposals or even to reconsider the whole idea of conversion or subdivision.

Sources of grants and preferential loans

Because of the favourable effect conversions and subdivisions have in assisting small business growth and economic regeneration a variety of groups offer grants and preferential loans (loans at favourable rates) to developers converting or subdividing property. Some are directed exclusively at small businesses developing property, some are only available for local authorities or charitable organizations such as Enterprise Agencies, others are available to all these groups (either in partnership or separately). This section gives a brief introduction to the most common sources of finance for developers purchasing buildings for conversion or undertaking conversion or subdivision work. Most forms of assistance are only given if the property to be developed is in certain geographical areas. This is a complex field; if you need more detail a comprehensive account is given in *Industrial Aids in the UK: A Businessman's Guide* by Mishka Bienkowski and Kevin Allen, published annually by the Centre for the Study of Public Policy, University of Strathclyde, Glasgow. If you think you might be eligible for a particular form of assistance, contact the organization concerned.

Although the list of possible sources may seem long, only firms in the designated areas will be eligible. Even some of the developers who have been eligible for these schemes have rejected the idea of applying for them, or withdrawn during negotiations, because of the length of time and amount of work involved in negotiating for what are sometimes fairly small amounts of money. At some schemes the delay may not be important or financial help may be necessary to make a scheme feasible. In these cases persistence is often rewarded. At other schemes where speed is essential or money is not a problem it may be beneficial to proceed without the possible delays generated by applying for assistance. In all cases gain as much information as you can from both the organization concerned and other groups who have applied for financial help from the scheme; their experiences can be an important guide to whether you should apply and the best ways to complete the appropriate forms.

Regional funds

Because of problems of high unemployment and economic depression the government has designated certain areas of the country as 'assisted areas'. There are two tiers of assisted areas. The first tier, the development areas, are eligible for both regional development grants and regional selective assistance. The second tier, intermediate areas (where unemployment is less severe), are eligible for only regional selective assistance. A list of the development and intermediate areas is given in Appendix 5.

Regional development grant   Regional development grants take the form of tax-free contributions towards capital expenditure, including premises for businesses and other private sector groups. The grant is available for the purchase and conversion of a building, but only for companies which will remain resident in the property. If other units are created the grant will be awarded for the area of the building which the developer's company occupies. Grants are intended primarily for manufacturing businesses but certain management, service, research and technical activities are also eligible. The rate of capital grant is set at 15 percent subject to a limit of £10,000 for each new job created (though this ceiling is not normally enforced for firms with less than 200 employees). Alternatively, labour-intensive projects can claim £3000 for each job the investment creates. For every approved application both the capital and the job grants will be calculated and firms will automatically be paid whichever is the greater.

Regional selective assistance   Regional selective assistance is discretionary but can be provided to business and other private sector groups for projects which provide or safeguard jobs in any part of the assisted areas. It has to be demonstrated that the project would not take place on the basis proposed without government assistance. Companies purchasing and converting a property for their own use are eligible but only if there is an increase in their company's employment. The amount of assistance is negotiated on a case-by-case basis and is fixed at the minimum sum needed to bring about the benefits associated with the project. Assistance is usually in the form of a grant; on very rare occasions preferential loans are provided. Regional selective assistance can be awarded in conjunction with regional development grant but eligible expenditure is then assessed net of regional development grant.

For further information on regional policy and inquiries on eligibility contact your regional office of the Department of Trade and Industry (addresses in Appendix 6). In Wales and Scotland contact the Welsh and Scottish Development Agencies (addresses in Appendix 1).

European funds

European assistance for economic and industrial regeneration was introduced under the European Regional Development Fund (ERDF) in March 1975. The fund provides financial assistance for regional industrial development in the assisted areas of the UK (see Appendix 5) and, through the non-quota section, in areas adversely affected by the restructuring of the textile, shipbuilding and steel industries.

European Regional Development Fund quota allowances ERDF money is available to public authorities, such as local authorities, for all or part of their investment in eligible schemes. Conversion schemes which provide new small units (up to 500 square metres: 5382 square feet) are eligible for a 20 percent grant. Infrastructure grants of up to 50 percent are available for approved capital costs such as roads, sewerage and water supply. These may be necessary to make some conversion schemes possible. Feasibility studies closely linked with the operations of ERDF money, such as those described above, are eligible for grants of up to 50 percent, or 70 percent in exceptional cases. For further details contact:

The Department of Trade and Industry
Regional Policy Division
Kingsgate House
66–74 Victoria Street
London SW1E 6SJ

Non-quota ERDF assistance Under the non-quota section of the ERDF, assistance is available to public authorities in assisted areas or textile, shipbuilding or steel closure areas. Although primarily intended for local authorities, non-quota money can also be awarded to joint ventures between the public and private sectors. Here the public sector contribution earns a 50 percent grant. This means that at conversion or subdivision schemes where local authorities become involved on a partnership basis half their financial contribution to the scheme will be provided by non-quota funds. If your scheme is barely feasible it may be possible to persuade your local authority to contribute some topping-up funds, because whatever amount they contribute will be matched by an equal non-quota contribution.

For further information contact the regional offices of the Department of the Environment (see Appendix 7).

Business Improvement Services Business Improvement Services grants are funded from non-quota ERDF money together with UK government funds. Specified areas of the UK affected by job losses in the shipbuilding, steel and textile industries are eligible for grants to help in the growth and development of small firms (for an exact definition of these areas contact the bodies below). Support is available for consultants or other organizations involved in providing assistance and consultancy advice on areas such as market research, finance, planning and marketing to small businesses. Conversion or subdivision schemes with a manager or other personnel providing these business support services are eligible for 55 percent grants on fixed assets such as plant, machinery and buildings involved in the provision of these services. In addition the personnel providing the business support services can be funded for 50 percent of their wages for up to four years.

The addresses of the appropriate contacts for this scheme are given in Appendix 8.

European Coal and Steel Community Loans European Coal and Steel Community (ECSC) loans are available to public bodies, private companies and other groups in areas where there have been steel or coal plant closures. There is no fixed definition of these areas. (Addresses of contacts are given in Appendix 9.) Loans of up to 50 percent of fixed capital costs are given to projects which provide at least two jobs in (or for workers from) coal or steel closure areas. Although jobs must be suitable for coal and steel workers they do not necessarily have to be taken by them. All conversion or subdivision schemes could be eligible if they create more than two administrative or managerial jobs associated with the scheme, or within the productive workforce at a conversion.

Urban funds

Inner Urban Areas Act (1978) funds Certain urban areas designated under the Inner Urban Areas Act 1978 are eligible for loans and grants which can assist with conversion and subdivision schemes. Designated areas are listed in Appendix 10.

Local authorities in these 'designated districts' can declare 'Improvement Areas' either industrial or commercial in character. Loans and grants are available for private businesses and other groups in the Improvement Areas under Sections 5 and 6 of the 1978 Act. Section 5 loans and grants are awarded at the discretion of the local authority for environmental improvement. The usual limits on these loans are 90 percent of project costs on commercial terms over 30 years. Examples of environmental improvement are sand blasting, rebuilding boundary walls, providing better access routes and other improvements to the external appearance of converted or subdivided buildings.

Section 6 of the Act provides grants for the improvement, conversion, modification or extension of industrial or commercial buildings, or the conversion of any building to industrial or commercial use. Grants are at the discretion of the local authority but usually do not exceed 50 percent of the project costs or £1000 per job that might be accommodated in the units created by a conversion or subdivision scheme. Assistance should not produce excessive returns for the developer of a scheme. If this is the case the level of assistance will be lowered accordingly.

Under Section 11, small firms in 'Special Areas' (designated by the 1978 Act) are eligible for grants to assist with interest payments on loans given for the purchase of land and/or buildings. This can include buildings purchased for conversion. The local authority decides the level of the grant but it is subject to a maximum of 12 percent of the loan. Grants are not made on loans received for Section 6 work (see above).

Urban Development Grants   Urban Development Grants (UDGs) are available for projects funded jointly by the private sector (including companies, charities, individuals and pension funds) and local authorities. Eligibility is primarily restricted to designated districts under the Inner Urban Areas Act 1978 (see Appendix 10) and also local authorities which have Enterprise Zones within their boundaries (see Appendix 2). Although the name suggests grant funding, loans or a combination of grants and loans are also given. Private sector funding must comprise the major part of the finance at a scheme; the ratio of private to public sector funding has been about 4:1. The objective of Urban Development Grants is to assist projects which contribute towards the economic, social or environmental conditions of an area and to financially assist projects of this nature which would otherwise not be feasible. Both conversion and subdivision schemes can contribute to all three aims of the UDG objectives. The rate of the award is the minimum necessary to implement the project. The UDG is payable to the local authority at a rate of not more than 75 percent of their financial contribution to the schemes.

For further details of the scheme in England contact the regional offices of the Department of the Environment (see Appendix 7), in Wales contact:

The Welsh Office
Cathays Park
Cardiff CF1 3NQ

A similar scheme exists in Scotland. It is called Local Enterprise Grants for Urban Projects (LEG-UP). In most respects the scheme is similar to UDGs, the exception being that the ratio of private to public funding can be at a lower ratio 2.5:1 minimum. There is no ceiling on the maximum amount of the award given to local authorities. For further details contact:

Project Manager
LEG-UP
Scottish Development Agency
120 Bothwell Street
Glasgow G2 7JP

Urban Programme   Each year local authorities in partnership and programme areas (see Appendix 10) receive urban programme money from central government. Finance is received for three types of project: industrial, environmental improvement and community development schemes. Under the first of these three categories local authorities are eligible to receive funds for conversion schemes which provide small units. Grants for 75 percent of their capital costs are given to schemes selected for support (the limit for capital costs is £140,000); the remaining 25 percent has to be provided by the local authority. For further details contact the regional offices of the Department of the Environment in England (see Appendix 7). In Wales contact:

Welsh Office Industry Department
Industry Department
Crown Buildings
Cathays Park
Cardiff CF1 3NQ

In Scotland contact:

Urban Renewal Unit
Scottish Development Department
St Andrews House
Regent Road
Edinburgh EH1 3DD

Enterprise Zones As part of an experimental project the government has designated 25 Enterprise Zones in various parts of the UK. Their aim is to increase economic activity by offering financial and tax incentives and by relaxing town planning and other administrative controls. The most important of these measures for most private sector groups contemplating conversion or subdivision is the exemption from paying rates on premises. The locations and contact addresses for the Enterprise Zones are given in Appendix 2.

Derelict land reclamation grants

Under the Derelict Land Act 1982 nearly all public and private groups can receive grants to improve the appearance of derelict land and bring it back into use. If during the development process it is necessary to demolish buildings to make a conversion or the utilization of further buildings feasible, the costs involved in demolition may be eligible for a derelict land grant. The grant specifically excludes the partial demolition of a building (or buildings) which would be part of the normal development. Be sure to distinguish between the two. Grants in Derelict Land Clearance Areas (usually defined as 'land so damaged by industrial or other development that it is incapable of beneficial use without treatment') and Assisted Areas (see Appendix 5) are available at the rate of 100 percent for local authorities and 80 percent for other bodies. Outside these areas the rate is 50 percent for both groups (except in National Parks and Areas of Outstanding Natural Beauty where local authorities receive a 75 percent grant).

Grants are administered by the Department of the Environment and further details can be obtained from their regional offices (see Appendix 7).

Rural funds

Council for Small Industries in Rural Areas   The Council for Small Industries in Rural Areas (CoSIRA) aims to improve the prosperity of small businesses in certain rural areas of England. Similar services are offered by the small business divisions of the Scottish and Welsh Development Agencies and the Local Enterprise Development Unit (LEDU) in Northern Ireland. Loans are to small firms in the manufacturing, service and tourism sectors for the acquisition (freehold or long lease) of buildings. This can include the acquisition of buildings for conversion. Loans are usually for up to 50 percent of purchase costs (for up to 20 years duration), with a minimum of £750 and maximum of £75,000.

CoSIRA also gives grants of up to 25 percent (maximum £50,000) for the conversion of suitable buildings for craft and light industrial units, where situated in English Rural Development Areas. Similar schemes are available in Wales and Scotland (under the 'Rural Workshops Scheme'). Grants in both areas are for 35 percent of project costs. In Scotland, Wales and Northern Ireland contact the Development Agencies, in England contact local CoSIRA offices. Addresses are given in Appendix 1 and 4 respectively.

Development Commission, Partnership Scheme   The Development Commission advises the Secretary of State on issues relating to economic and social development in rural areas and since 1984 has had powers to offer grants to local authorities. They will enter into a 50:50 partnership with local authorities in rural areas (mainly areas with a central town of less than 10,000 population) to convert industrial property to provide small units. Rental or sale income is then shared between the local authority and the Development Commission.

For further information contact:

> The Development Commission
> 11 Cowley Street
> London SW1 3NA

Miscellaneous funds

Architectural Heritage Fund   The Architectural Heritage Fund gives loans to charities to refurbish historic buildings for resale; this can include conversion schemes. Loans are usually given over a two-year period repayable at 5 percent per annum interest for 50 percent of refurbishment costs.

For further details contact:

> The Administrator
> The Architectural Heritage Fund
> 17 Carlton House Terrace
> London SW1 5AW

British Steel Corporation (Industry) Ltd BSC Industry aims to assist economic growth in 17 areas where steel closures have occurred. Most of these areas are eligible for low interest European Coal and Steel Community funds (see the section on European funds, p.68) and many also receive aid because they have been designated as assisted areas. In each of its 17 areas BSC Industry offers assistance to any private sector company or group with finding premises, and gives technical advice and guidance on preparing applications for local authority or government assistance; this can include assistance for conversion and subdivision schemes.

For further details contact:

British Steel Corporation (Industry) Ltd
NLA Tower
12 Addiscombe Road
Croydon CR9 3JH

British Technology Group The British Technology Group was established to promote innovation and investment in British industry. Within the English Assisted Areas the Group has a wider role than its normal technological focus: it helps all businesses which have growth potential and can improve their efficiency by modernization or rationalization. This can include money for businesses to purchase premises for conversion if this is part of an overall improvement programme.

For further details contact the British Technology Group (addresses in Appendix 1).

English Estates English Estates' prime concern is the direct provision of industrial and commercial premises, in the Assisted Areas (see Appendix 5) and also in certain rural locations. They also arrange mortgages for private sector companies and groups with financial institutions at favourable interest rates to purchase property for conversion.

For further details contact your nearest English Estates' office (addresses in Appendix 11).

Historic Buildings Council The Historic Buildings Council gives grants for the upkeep of Grade I and II listed buildings. Money is available to public and private sector groups for major structural repairs; these could be part of a conversion or subdivision scheme. Applicants should usually have owned the building for at least two years, but in special cases, such as the purchase of a building to prevent further deterioration and undertake restoration, exceptions may occur. The minimum amount of the grant is £4000 and private developers can obtain grants of up to 40 percent of eligible costs.

Further details can be obtained from the Historic Buildings Council's national offices. In England these are at:

25 Savile Row
London W1X 2BT

In Scotland:

> 25 Drumsheugh Gardens
> Edinburgh EH3 7RN

In Wales:

> The Welsh Office
> Crown Buildings
> Cathays Park
> Cardiff CF1 3NQ

Local Authority Assistance Many local authorities, anxious to encourage economic development and employment growth, offer grants and loans to all private sector companies and groups for the acquisition, subdivision and conversion of property. Authorities are often particularly keen to support 'small unit' schemes. The amount and types of grants and loans vary throughout the UK. Further details for all areas can be obtained by contacting the local authority's industrial development officer.

NCB Enterprise Ltd NCB Enterprise Ltd was created in 1985 to ensure that new jobs were created in areas where pits have had to close. The company is currently supported by funding of £20m. It can provide loans to businesses which may be used for the purchase of premises for conversion. A full list of NCB Enterprise Ltd area contacts is given in Appendix 12.

Inland Revenue allowances

In addition to the various sources of grants and loans given above, various forms of tax relief are available for developers converting or subdividing property. Your accountant should be fully aware of these and either he or your local Inland Revenue office will be able to give you further information.

It is possible to obtain tax relief for capital expenditure incurred on the construction or conversion of buildings to be used for productive, manufacturing or processing trades. For all sizes of premises the rate is 25 percent on expenditure incurred before 1 April 1986, but after this date there will be no initial allowance. In all cases the writing-down allowance is usually fixed at 4 percent per annum; this will be the only allowance given after 1 April 1986.

Many of the costs associated with relocating an existing business to a conversion scheme are eligible for corporate tax relief. It is possible to defer capital gains tax incurred when selling your existing premises if the proceeds are invested in constructing new accommodation; this includes converting property.

The Community Programme

The Community Programme, administered by the Manpower Services Commission, may be a possible source not so much of finance as of getting work done free of charge.

The Programme is part of the MSC's job creation package, and, through sponsor agencies, provides work for unemployed people. Programme workers employed by the scheme undertake a range of tasks, including many associated with the conversion and subdivision of property, which have a benefit to the community.

There are broad guiding principles to what can and cannot be undertaken within the Programme. There is considerable regional and local variation in the exact interpretation of these principles. A key principle in the context of conversion and subdivision is that there must be no direct private gain. There can, though, be 'incidental gain'. Basically this means that the use of the Community Programme for building works is restricted to local authorities and other non-profit-making organizations. However, environmental work associated with conversion and subdivision, including, for example, site clearance and tidying up, erection of fences, painting and external cleaning, is eligible for the private developer. In these cases the gain to the private sector would be incidental and is an environmental gain for the community. As there is an 'operational cost' associated with each Community Programme worker of approximately £450, paid for by the MSC, some if not all of the materials required in such work can also be provided by the Programme.

Many developers have successfully made use of the Community Programme, particularly for environmental work. It operates at a local level and all inquiries should be directed to the local Programme Area Office. Frequently these are located in the local Job Centre, to whom your initial inquiry should be directed.

Key points

1 Contact as many organizations as possible who may be able to assist financially.
2 Give special attention to agencies who offer grants and preferential loans.
3 Put together a prospectus for your proposal.
4 Consult your accountant about the tax-effectiveness of your scheme.
5 Apply to the Community Programme for assistance.

Chapter 8

Marketing

Creating an image

Decisions on how to market a conversion or subdivision should be taken at an early stage in the planning of any development. During all your discussions with the different groups concerned with the conversion or subdivision you will create an image about your development. This image must reflect the final appearance, layout and character of the development. The term 'image' may sound a little grand but it is important to remember that when you eventually offer units on the market, they will be promoted on the basis of two or three key features such as low rental levels, high quality accommodation, excellent central services or prime location. These features and the way in which they are promoted will create the development's image. It is better to be known as 'the development in a good location creating low cost (or high quality) accommodation for small businesses' than simply 'those new units down by the ringroad'. Ensure that the image you create is precise enough to present an attractive picture of the final development to your target market, but never make the image so precise that it appeals to only a portion of your market. General details are fine when describing a development, but be careful not to be too precise and thus exclude some of your prospective tenants.

Developing a marketing strategy

Whilst there should be few problems in finding tenants for a development if market research has been carried out carefully, it is still important to develop a marketing strategy. A successful marketing strategy will slowly increase public awareness about a scheme, and will culminate in a modest press launch or increased advertising and media coverage. Your strategy should involve contacting several different local organizations who can help in the promotion of your development.

Timing your marketing strategy is important. Some developers try to culminate their marketing activities and attract prospective tenants before all building work is finished. Tenants are then ready to occupy the units as soon as they are completed, providing an immediate rental income. However, showing tenants round a partially completed site or unfinished units can create problems. Prospective tenants find it difficult to visualize the final site or the units being produced. It is usually most successful to show prospective tenants units when all structural work has been completed.

Timing marketing activities for a particular season or month of the year seems to be unnecessary. The fluctuating fortunes of the housing market, with a peak of interest in spring and a relative void in winter, do not occur within the commercial and industrial market. Interest in business premises tends to remain reasonably constant throughout the year. It might be worth considering a spring or summer launch as this will enable clients to see your property at its best; but the vagaries of the British climate make even this minor consideration an uncertainty.

Creating a well coordinated marketing strategy can be time consuming. It involves contacting many different groups at different times during the development process. Draw up a marketing strategy diary to ensure you contact all these different groups at the most appropriate time. A typical marketing strategy diary is shown in Table 8.1. It makes the maximum possible use of free sources of advertising and promotion and culminates in a modest press launch. The latter may seem ambitious for a small development, but if you contact all the groups shown it is often the quickest and most efficient approach. The offer of free food and drink will usually attract the appropriate interested parties. The extent to which you undertake these activities will depend upon the size of your development. Some elements of the strategy, such as putting up billboards and contacting the local authority, Enterprise Agencies, and business organizations, are essential. Other elements may be less important at smaller developments. The style of any marketing strategy will depend upon the particular circumstances of the development.

Promoting property

The marketing strategy diary shown in Table 8.1 describes a variety of groups which can be used to promote your development. The help which they can offer in informing potential clients of your development, and the role they can play in the overall marketing strategy described earlier, is outlined below.

The local media

As the marketing diary shows, the local media can play a significant role in promoting your development. This publicity can usually be obtained free. The term local media includes local newspapers (both daily and the free weeklies), other local community broadsheets, local radio stations and local television. With the exception of television, who may only be interested in the press launch, all these media outlets are usually eager for 'local news'. The creation of jobs and local development which your activities will involve can provide them with very newsworthy material.

Try to gain as much media interest as possible at the very start of the project. Tell them as much as you can about the development and its job creation potential. Promote the image of the development. Make sure you convey details about the type of units you are developing. Your initial meeting will be important. It enables them to

Table 8.1 A typical marketing strategy diary

Weeks until launch	Promotion activity	Progress on building work
	Press release to the local media to announce the start of building work at the development. Stress the image you want to promote about the completed scheme.	Start
	(a) One progress report to local media stressing success and interest already shown by local business. (b) Invite the local Chamber of Commerce and other business organizations to hold their weekly or monthly meeting at your premises when work is completed – estimate a date.	Mid point progress report
As early as possible	Invite a celebrity to the press launch.	
6	Finalize a date and arrange details for the press launch.	4 weeks until completion
4	(a) Confirm the date of Chamber of Commerce or other business organization's visit to your premises. (b) Invite the industrial development officer and local councillors to view the premises.	2 weeks until completion
3	(a) Release a progress report and invitations to the press launch for the local media stating that work is nearly completed. (b) Invite potential new tenants to come and examine premises. Also enclose a letter inviting them to the press launch. (c) Invite all other interested groups to the press launch.	1 week until completion
2	(a) Release details about the units to the local authority, Enterprise Agencies, business organizations and estate agents. (b) Put up billboards (only *x units* left). (c) Industrial development officer, some of his staff and local councillors view the premises.	Work completed
1	Local Chamber of Commerce and other local business organizations hold their weekly meeting at the development.	
	PRESS LAUNCH	
+1	Advertise in local press (if necessary).	
+2	Advertise in local press (if necessary).	

realize that you can provide them with a newsworthy story. A progress report released midway through the building work will remind the media that your development is still in progress. Any amusing incidents or snippets discussing the level of interest already shown by local businesses will usually merit some sort of mention. A press embargo, which only allows the release of information at a specified date, will cut out the element of competition that sometimes occurs in local media coverage. It also allows the media time to prepare a better, more considered article.

Further details of the role the media play at the press launch are given in the next section. If you do not hold a press launch you should still use the local media to promote your development. A press launch will enable you to gain this coverage free on the news pages of a paper or news bulletins on the radio. If you have to advertise you will be paying for coverage which may be hidden away on the less well read advertising columns of a paper or missed while someone was out making the tea during the radio advertisements.

At some developments, particularly very small schemes with only two or three units, a press launch may be inappropriate. Even at these schemes it is still worth while sending out a press release or inviting the local media to your development. Every development should be able to generate some media 'news' interest.

It may also be useful to supplement this with some advertising. One way of avoiding paying all these costs yourself is to initiate a joint advertisement. Persuade all the builders, contractors and other groups involved in the construction of your development to purchase advertising space in the local newspaper or on radio. Full-page advertisements of contractors 'wishing luck on your development' or 'pleased to have been involved in the development' are very popular. It may be possible to get your first tenants to contribute to this type of campaign. The advertisement will bring their name to the public's attention as well, so they should not be too reticent in contributing.

Local authorities

Many of the activities undertaken during your development will have involved contact with the local authority. You will probably have met the industrial development officer. They are approached by many businesses looking for premises and will be a useful point of contact in your search for suitable tenants. It may be appropriate to invite the industrial development officer and interested local councillors to your development; this will help them recall details more readily when approached by potential tenants. In the marketing strategy diary this group was invited to visit developments two weeks before the press launch.

Many local authorities now compile registers of vacant premises which they distribute free of charge to businesses looking for property. Make sure your premises are included on their list. The industrial development officer will be able to tell you which department to contact if your local authority produces one of these registers.

Local business clubs

Some small business associations, clubs and Chambers of Commerce or Trade also compile registers of vacant premises. Even if they do not produce a formal register, they may well know of members looking for new accommodation.

All these groups have continuing contact with the local business community either directly by membership or indirectly by trading contacts with other companies. For this reason it is often worth joining one of these groups yourself. Invite them to hold their weekly or monthly meeting at your development. You can talk to them about its progress and the possibilities which conversion or subdivision can offer their businesses. A change in venue or a new speaker will be a very attractive proposition.

Like all the promotional work you will be undertaking, the people you talk to will help to circulate information about your development. Even if their members are not looking for accommodation now, they may know of others who are, or they may be looking for your type of accommodation in the future.

Enterprise Agencies and small business advice groups

Both these groups are approached by businesses seeking help and advice. Some of these inquiries will be from companies looking for property. Send all these groups information about your development and invite them to the press launch. A list of your local Enterprise Agencies can be obtained from their coordinating body, Business in the Community (address in Appendix 1).

Billboards

It is essential to put up billboards advertising the availability of small business units. Surprisingly they are one of the most successful methods of advertising vacant industrial and commercial property. Signs advertising vacant units to traffic passing a development have been very successful in attracting tenants. At some developments, which have maintained full occupancy, this has been the only method used to attract new tenants. The cheap cost of billboards makes their use highly advisable. Once again it is important to be positive. Use the phrase 'only *x units* left', not simply 'units to let'.

Estate agents

Estate agents are one of the most common ways of promoting industrial property. Their use can be problematical. As their fee structure is based on 10 percent of first-year rents or between 1.5 and 2.5 percent of the purchase price of the freehold of a property, they may be tempted to promote only more expensive properties. If your units are relatively inexpensive it may be worth considering some of the other methods already described.

Estate agents provide other services in addition to finding prospective tenants. They will interview prospective tenants to make sure they meet your requirements. They will take up a client's bankers and trade references. These will give an indication of the company's current position and probable future viability.

When you engage an estate agent to advertise your property they will normally send you a 'standard fee letter' which outlines their conditions of service. Read it very carefully. Many include a phrase which states that 'fees are chargeable in the event of a disposal irrespective of the manner in which the purchaser was introduced to the property'. This means that if you sign an agreement with them and subsequently find a tenant yourself (without their help or involvement) you will still be charged the relevant fee. If you are promoting property yourself as well as using estate agents, ensure your agreement with them does not include this clause.

Brochures

All the groups you visit when promoting a conversion or subdivision scheme should be given a brochure containing details of the development. The brochure should emphasize all the advantages of a scheme and provide details about the sizes of units, rents, facilities and business support services available. Deciding when to produce these brochures will depend on particular local circumstances. Pictures of a site and completed units are preferable to artists' impressions, but if builders are still active it may be impossible to take suitable pictures. Glossy brochures with pictures can be expensive: £800–£1000 per 1000 is not unusual. Quite eye-catching leaflets can be produced for much less than this. Brochures will be required for all the promotional groups you contact, prospective tenants and guests at a press launch.

When the development is occupied a brochure with all the occupants' names, their activities and a map of how to find them (and the site) can also be distributed by tenants to their customers and suppliers. Many tenants are often willing to contribute to the production costs of these brochures.

A press launch

The idea of a press launch at a small development may seem rather extravagant but a press launch can be very cost-effective in terms of both time and money. A press launch can act as a 'thank you' party for many of the groups which might have been involved in your development. It can also be used as a method to entice prospective tenants to look around a site. Tenants are often impressed by a 'high profile' opening. They will want to be part of a successful development and a press launch will create this image.

Arrange a press launch for one or two weeks after work at the development has been completed. This will give you enough time to tidy the site and prepare for the launch. It will also ensure that some tenants will already be operating their businesses in the new units. Preparation for the launch should begin several weeks before it takes place, but do not finalize a date until you are sure that all building work at the site will have been completed. Choose a date for the launch when no other major local, national and international events are due to occur. If nothing else happens on the day and news is thin, you may make the front page!

Extra media attention and interest in a development will be generated if a celebrity is present. Celebrities often require several weeks' or even months' notice so contact them as early as possible. There are two broad groups of celebrities you might consider: local distinguished dignitaries, such as the mayor, an MP or chairman of a business organization, or local media celebrities, such as sportsmen, actors or television personalities. Dignitaries may be willing to discuss and emphasize the development whereas media celebrities will promote more press coverage and greater attendance amongst interested groups.

Selecting the right celebrity is important. Two recent incidents demonstrate why. In September 1981 when Geoffrey Boycott was dropped from the Yorkshire cricket team, West Yorkshire Metropolitan County Council engaged him at very short notice for promotional work in London. Before Mr Boycott arrived the venue was filled to capacity with the national press and other interested groups. The event gained considerable coverage on the television news and in the national newspapers. Unfortunately all the coverage related to Geoffrey Boycott's cricketing activities; West Yorkshire Council barely gained a mention. A similar incident occurred during the national miners' strike in 1984 when Peter Walker, the energy minister, attended a long-standing engagement to open some small business units in the Midlands. He was interviewed by television news and the national newspapers, but the lengthy coverage which was given to his speech did not include any details of the small business accommodation. Both these events were unfortunate victims of particular circumstances, but they emphasize the importance of finding the right type of celebrity who will generate interest in your development. Similarly they illustrate how even the most carefully laid plans can go wrong.

About three weeks before the event, send a letter to the local media personnel, whom you will have already met, inviting them to the launch. Also send invitations to other media groups such as the editors of small business magazines, local business papers, financial journals and the small business or financial editors of national newspapers or journals. Enclose with each invitation a press release, embargoed until the press launch, which gives full details of the development and the high level of interest that has already been shown. Even if the media do not attend the launch, they will probably publish an article based on the information given to them. When writing your press release bear in mind that the less rewriting the journalists have to do, the more likely they are to publish the story.

Invitations for the launch together with details about the development should also be sent to other interested groups (see list below). Adequate details can usually be contained on one sheet of A4 paper. Include the two or three main points you are using to promote an image for your development and provide details about the units: sizes, facilities, services, location, etc. Also give details of any tenants already on site. Include a location map of the development as well as your brochure. Enclosing a 'reply slip' will provide a useful guide to the number of people to expect. Although this can never be completely accurate, it will enable you to give the caterers some idea of the numbers involved.

The type of development being undertaken and particular local circumstances will determine whom you should invite. The key groups will include:

1 local media
2 national media (if appropriate)
3 Lord Mayor and/or local councillors
4 industrial development officer
5 representatives from local business clubs
6 representatives from local Enterprise Agencies
7 representatives from organizations assisting local business
8 anyone who provided finance for the development
9 estate agents (if formally engaged)
10 prospective tenants
11 local bank managers.

All these people will directly and indirectly help to promote your development. Local bank managers have been added to the groups already discussed because they may be able to provide finance for your prospective tenants at some time in the future.

Press launches are usually best conducted at lunchtime. A buffet lunch with wine should be provided. Some people may only come for the lunch but at least they will have visited the site. Have copies of your brochure describing the development available for distribution to all visitors.

Two speeches are usually adequate to inform all the guests verbally about the development. In your speech you should thank everyone who contributed to the conversion and subdivision and then go on to stress its main assets and the contribution it will make to the local economy. If you can get a second speaker to endorse your views, this will help to emphasize the value of the development. This might be the invited celebrity, a representative from a local business organization or some other respected dignatory.

Promotion after the press launch

By the time of the press launch you should have a number of businesses already interested in your workspace project. Advertising one week after the launch is a useful follow-up reminder to anyone who may still be thinking about whether or not to apply. An advertisement two weeks after the launch is optional and will depend upon the success of your earlier efforts.

Even if at this stage all the units are not filled, do not despair; it takes time for news of your development to circulate. If your market research was carried out successfully and units were designed to meet the demand you found, you should have nothing to worry about. Your feasibility study will have anticipated voids.

If, despite all your best efforts, you cannot get tenants for the property, it is still possible to avoid some of the overhead costs by applying for rate relief on the premises. After the subdivision of existing property or the construction of new property is completed, Inland Revenue valuation officers can be asked to assess or reassess the rateable value of new units. Any parts which subsequently remain empty after conversion or subdivision can apply to the local authority's rating department for reduced rates on the grounds that they are separate unused premises.

Key points

1 At the start of any development decide on the two or three key features you will use to promote an image.
2 Develop a coordinated marketing strategy.
3 Use a marketing strategy diary.
4 Contact the local media.
5 Contact as many organizations as possible who can directly or indirectly promote your development. These will include:
   a the local authority
   b local business clubs
   c Enterprise Agencies
   d small business advice groups.
6 Read all contracts to employ estate agents carefully.
7 Put up billboards.
8 If applicable, use a press launch as the culmination of your marketing activities.
9 Throughout all your marketing activities be confident and promote the image of a flourishing and successful development.

Chapter 9

Management

A sound approach to management is vital if the full potential of a conversion or subdivision scheme is to be realized. Good management will ensure rental income is maximized, buildings are properly maintained and day-to-day administration is efficient. A variety of approaches to management can be adopted. Different developers include different elements in their management strategy. This chapter outlines these alternatives and indicates procedures which should be employed in developing individual strategies.

General management considerations

There is a wide range of items which need consideration in the early stages of developing a management strategy. These will include:

1 management style; who should do it
2 leases, licences and lettings
3 rent collection and the recovery of other charges
4 management and the provision of services
5 monitoring the development.

Although this list is not exhaustive, it provides the key areas which will be discussed separately below.

Management style

Management style is a key element in the success of any conversion or subdivision scheme. Although style will vary between different types of development, the broad approach must be one which is in tune with the needs of small businesses. At small units a flexible, informal approach is often required to encourage small and new start-up companies to respond to their changing needs and problems. New start-ups will not necessarily have developed the business discipline associated with a more mature company. They may not even be available to pay the rent on the predetermined day.

A structured yet informal, rather than overly formal, management style is the key to any successful development. Such a style can respond quickly and sympathetically to the tenants whilst maintaining the overall management objectives of the development.

Managing the development

The precise management method adopted will depend on the specific background of a development, its overall purpose, the developer and possibly the funding agency. A highly commercial development may leave all management functions to an agent whilst a scheme initiated by a group on a cooperative basis may adopt a communal approach to management. Experience suggests that greater success is likely to be achieved in cases where the developer and manager are in close communication, or are one and the same person. Commitment is assured when the developer is closely involved in the management of the property.

Managing a scheme can take up a considerable amount of time which may be employed more effectively in other activities. Some developers simply do not wish to be involved in the day-to-day running of the property. Where developers want to be involved in the overall management of a scheme but not the day-to-day functions, it is possible to share or split this activity. The day-to-day lower order functions are undertaken by a part-time manager or tenant such as a typing or staff agency whilst the higher order functions such as organizing lettings and leases remains the responsibility of the developer.

Where the developer does not become involved in managing the property, a manager should be hired. It is vital to choose the right person. At conversion and subdivision schemes undertaken by local authorities and other groups trying to assist local small business growth, a manager will play an active role in helping tenants overcome their business problems. At a private development managers usually play a more passive role and are mainly concerned with administering the scheme on a day-to-day basis, but even here managers can often become involved in helping tenants. Some private developers have found that if they offer a business advice service it can be an important attraction for new tenants. The manager will be the key to the success of a development and in all probability will help to contribute to the success of the tenant businesses themselves. A successful small unit manager will be a lively, but not pushy individual with a commitment to the project. At developments offering advice to businesses he or she should also have wide business experience and be committed to helping small businesses.

The right person with all these attributes and business experience will cost around £12,000 or more per annum. This may encourage some developers to consider other ways of obtaining a good manager. For companies subdividing or converting property this may be an ideal opportunity for a member of staff who is approaching retirement or looking for a new direction in work content. Alternatively, managing small units may prove a suitable and rewarding occupation for a local business person who has taken early retirement. In this case it is frequently possible to negotiate a salary more appropriate to the income of the development. Where developments are undertaken by agencies such as Enterprise Agencies or local authorities, consideration should be given to the use of secondees either from a local authority department or from a local company. An experienced manager can often be obtained in this way at minimal cost. However, all secondees return eventually to their parent organization; as a result the continuity and stability of management is often affected. Stability is essential to the successful management of small units and is an area worthy of careful consideration when deciding who will manage the scheme.

Leases, licences and lettings

Lettings should be controlled by a formal agreement. This is usually a licence or lease. Before discussing these in more detail it is worth noting that recently many developers have adopted a far more informal system of lettings based on either a simple gentleman's agreement about conditions of occupancy or a slightly more formal system using letters of agreement. In the latter case the letter would specify the period of notice required on either side. Whilst offering extreme flexibility, this type of agreement offers little security to either party and is to be encouraged only in cases where minimal services are provided by the developer or as a means of filling space prior to or during the development of the scheme.

The licence is becoming increasingly popular with landlords because it offers a very flexible easy-in easy-out system of lettings (a typical licence is shown in Appendix 13). By using the licence system many developments can offer immediate occupancy to prospective tenants, because licences can be implemented on site without any delays. Additionally it can remove the need for solicitors and other costs associated with more formal agreements. The site manager will need to understand the system adequately, explain it to prospective tenants and effect completion of the licence agreement. It is important to remember that normally a licence is not a legal interest in premises although there does remain considerable confusion over the status of a licence, and protection under the Landlord and Tenant Act. Neither can a licence be sold at a premium as is the case with a lease.

The lease is still the most common form of contract in spite of its greater formality. Many tenants feel it gives them greater security. Small start-ups often do not consider failure and the need for flexible arrangements. A variety of off-the-shelf leases are available from the Oyez Law Stationery Office, head office:

Oyez House
237 Long Lane
Bermondsey
London SE1
01 407 8055

These specimen leases, available for about 50p, ensure the lease will meet all current legal requirements. In more difficult cases it is probably beneficial to contact a solicitor.

Both the licence and lease are designed to cover the basic conditions and terms between the landlord and tenant. Consequently every contract must contain:

1 the names of the landlord (lessor) and tenant (lessee)
2 an agreement between the lessor to let the property and the lessee to take possession of the property
3 a detailed description of the property (if necessary using plans)
4 the rental to be paid (including frequency and payment date).

In addition there are several points which need consideration when drawing up an agreement. These points are worth considering whatever type of agreement is used, they will ensure that the implications of the agreement are carefully considered and worked out.

Terms of lease Be quite clear and explicit about the terms of the lease. These will include the level of rent, frequency of payment, date of commencement, duration and, perhaps most important, who will take responsibility for the various costs and liabilities associated with the building. These may include rates, repairs, insurance and any other liabilities associated with various property-related agencies. Make sure the tenant is aware of these.

Length of lease Offer alternative lease lengths. Leases can be for any length of time but three years is usually the shortest. Five, nine or twenty-one years are common lengths. Many developers offer a range of lease lengths to suit the individual needs of tenants. Joint use of the licence and lease can allow a very flexible package with agreements ranging from one month to twenty-one years.

Rent review The implementation of a rent review and the time period between reviews must be stated in the agreement. Rents should be reviewed periodically. Commonly reviews are every three years, but they can be at other periods. Sometimes they are fixed to one of the Retail Price Index measures, but there are several other different price measures. Choosing the 'right one' can be very difficult.

Some reviews specify the exact amount of future rental increases. For example, a nine-year lease may include clauses which fix the rent at £1000 per annum for the first three years, £1300 for years four to six and £1600 for years seven to nine. In this form the tenants know exactly what their liabilities are and can trade accordingly.

Use It is normal for a lease to contain restrictions on the use of the workspace. Restrictions may relate to specific businesses or to nuisances, such as noise or noxious fumes, associated with specific activities. These use restrictions must of course reflect those imposed by the local planning authority (see Chapter 5). For example, it may be necessary to specify the times at which the building may be used if planning consent imposes such a condition.

Change of use The lease should specify what, if any, permission will be required for the use of space to be changed. It is worth giving some consideration to this issue because in small unit developments the close proximity of users can create problems if they are not compatible. This may be particularly relevant in subdivisions where the developer's firm's image is important and bad neighbours may affect that image.

Subletting It may be wise to control any subletting of all or part of a unit. This can be achieved simply by requiring the tenant to obtain formal approval before subletting. It is worth being flexible in the actual operation of this condition because 'shared space', a form of subletting where a friend or business associate 'lives in' the unit whilst in the very early stages of developing their own business, is an increasingly popular activity. The 'shared space' idea can be very beneficial to the new start-up whilst at the same time providing the landlord with a prospective new tenant.

Repairs and other 'usual covenants' The term 'usual covenants' is used in leases to cover a wide range of circumstances. These may include:

1 the payment of rent, rates and any other taxes
2 maintenance and repair of the property
3 landlord access to examine the conditions of the property
4 repossession in the event of non-payment of rent.

All these need checking and clarifying with the tenants. Arguments can arise about levels of maintenance and liabilities associated with repair. For example, who is liable for the repair of a major structural defect in the building during the life of the lease? The issue of repair and maintenance is of particular significance in older property where defects can be particularly expensive to rectify.

Alterations and improvements It will be necessary to specify any restrictions which are appropriate to control modifications to the unit by tenants. The tenant may wish to erect items such as additional partitioning, make a store-room or install dust extraction equipment. The lease must state precisely whether this type of activity is possible and whether the landlord requires complete reinstatement at the end of the tenancy. Reinstatement requires the removal of all items installed by the tenant, returning the unit to the same condition as when it was first let. In other cases where the tenant has improved the property by providing facilities which become an integral part of the unit, such as an independent heating system, the lease should state how the tenant will receive compensation for such works.

Service charges Service charges are those charges additional to the rent which cover costs associated with running the units. It is important to differentiate between these charges, the rental and other services which may be bought by the tenant when required. The services themselves are discussed on page 91. Service charges will be subject to reviews which, because of their nature, may be at different intervals to the review of rent. Because of the unpredictability of many of the costs of these services it may be appropriate to include a clause in a lease or any other type of agreement which states these will be reviewed as and when necessary.

Selecting tenants

Many developers view the process of tenant selection as one based on intuition. They believe they can judge suitability simply by talking to the prospective tenant. Others take a more formal approach to screening tenants. Whichever approach is adopted it is important to realize that, in any development for small firms, tenant compatibility in terms of personality as well as activity is vital. Factors to be investigated when selecting tenants will include:

1 trading viability; this should include taking at least two trade references
2 financial viability; this should include taking at least one banker's reference
3 previous trading or employment history
4 detailed information on the nature of the business to be performed; special attention should be paid to equipment and machinery to be used in respect particularly of noise, fire risk and required floor loadings.

It is vital to establish a set procedure for tenants who wish to apply for space in your development so that both you and they know exactly where each party stands. Many developers set up a management system to deal with this element of the scheme. This will include a standard application form for prospective tenants of the units, an example of which is given in Appendix 14. As well as details of the company it should also identify the tenants' needs in terms, for example, of electricity and floor loadings.

Rents collection and the recovery of other charges

Rental levels

The initial market research for the project will have given valuable information about rental levels and approaches to charging both for space and service charges. For the private developer the primary consideration must be to set rents at a high enough level to earn a reasonable rate of return on the investment and yet low enough to attract and maintain reliable tenants. In the case of groups such as Enterprise Agencies or local authorities rents should be fixed at a level which permits the units to fulfil the authority's policy (for example, to encourage new start-up companies) whilst keeping the level of subsidy to a minimum. Market research and the initial assessment of viability will have taken this into account and derived a figure for the probable rental level at the scheme. Although major deviations from this initial, well founded estimate are not advisable, they are possible. The final standard of the units, the location or even image may allow an upward (or downward) adjustment of rental levels. Unlike newly constructed units, built to a common specification, it is often very difficult for tenants to compare units at subdivided or converted buildings with other properties they have seen. Each conversion and subdivision will be unique.

Many developers choose to offer initial rent incentives to new tenants either as part of the formal rental agreement or more commonly on an individual basis reflecting the circumstances of particular tenants. Such incentives can include:

1 an initial rent-free period of about four weeks to allow tenants to settle in and organize their space
2 a first-year rent at a lower level than would otherwise be the case.

Whilst this practice is quite common it can lead to animosity between tenants if it is not applied uniformly. It may also create difficulties for the new start-up when the 'free' period comes to an end.

It may be appropriate to consider offering different rents in various parts of a development. The attributes of individual units and the potential uses to which they can be put should affect rental levels. Units which are suitable for commercial and office use will command a higher rent than those for manufacturing. Units which are not on the ground floor will normally command a lower rental if used for light manufacturing because of poorer access. The size of the spaces frequently influences the unit cost rentals charged; the cost of smaller units is usually more per square foot than larger units. Very small spaces under 250 square feet are commonly at a premium and can consequently be assessed at higher rental levels.

Presentation of rents

The presentation of rents is important because it will influence the image of the development to prospective tenants. Whilst industrial property has traditionally been let on an annual rental per square foot or metre of space exclusive of all other charges, alternatives are now being used in small unit developments. Other combinations are possible. Four possible methods are outlined below. Each has its advantages and disadvantages.

1 *Rentals quoted in £s per square foot exclusive of other charges.* This is the traditional approach. It understates the real cost of acquiring and running the space because it gives no indication of the other charges. Frequently the tenant is not in a position to calculate the extent of these other charges and may therefore grossly underestimate the running cost of the property. It does on the other hand offer the tenant the flexibility to buy in as much or as little of other services as required. It can make the collection of charges very bitty and hence be more time-consuming for the management. Many developers give an indication of likely additional costs in their prospectus for the property.

2 *Rentals quoted in £s per square foot inclusive of all charges.* This allows the tenant to see total outgoings per week or month and budget accordingly. It is easier to manage because there are less individual items of payment. The one drawback of this method is that it can make space seem very expensive. Initially it is more complex for the management as it necessitates very careful assessment of all charges and their allocation between units.

3 *A lump sum for a given amount of space inclusive or exclusive of all charges.* This approach to presenting property costs is becoming increasingly popular. It allows the tenant to assess the full weekly or monthly property cost of their business very easily. Particularly in the case of a new start-up, space is viewed in terms of 'about the size of a double garage' rather than a specific square footage. Consequently an inclusive lump sum cost per week or month is more meaningful and easily appreciated. If the charge includes the service charges as well, the small business knows the property costs exactly and can hence trade accordingly.

4 *Payment on an hourly or daily basis.* In a few cases of managed workshops run largely by local authorities, and known as 'Enterprise Workshops', fully serviced and equipped space is let on a daily basis over a contracted period.

Whichever approach is adopted, it is important to explain fully which costs are included in any agreement. Although these details will be itemized in the lease or licence, it is in the management's interest to be sure the tenant is fully aware of them. They may for example be included in a 'package' given to the tenant when taking over a unit. Very few people have a clear idea or an appreciation of metric and non-metric measurement so it is always better to quote in £s per square foot rather than metres. A unit offered at £1.50 per square foot appears a far more attractive proposition than the same unit offered at £16.15 per square metre.

The collection of rent and charges is best done on site either weekly or monthly in advance. Managers should always try to ensure that they have at least one month's rent in hand at any time. With a monthly payment system ask tenants for two months' rent on arrival and then collect rents monthly. This should allow you to resolve non-payment problems within the time period of this advanced rent. Monthly rental collection also allows companies which get into difficulties to be identified quickly and helped or counselled. Frequently when small businesses seek advice about financial problems it is too late to take remedial action.

Collection of rents can be an arduous and difficult task. Some managers like to remain in contact with tenants but find it beneficial to delegate all financial issues to groups such as estate agents, business service agencies, typing agencies or any other group helping to manage the site. In this way they can discuss day-to-day problems without touching on the sometimes sensitive area of financial costs. Some site managers prefer to collect rents themselves because it allows a regular point of contact between landlord (or his representative) and the tenants. This can be a useful and informal link for the provision of information and business advice, and for monitoring progress.

A book-keeping system is essential to record and monitor charges. It will also provide written evidence in disputes about late or non-payment of rents.

A variety of book-keeping systems are available, ranging from a simple card index to the use of a micro-computer. Whatever system is used it should record payments recovered for rent, service charges, electricity, and all other financial transactions between landlord and tenant.

Services and service charges

The level of services which should be provided will depend entirely on the approach which the developer/manager wishes to take after evaluating market research information. There are five approaches which can be taken:

No service provision The developer provides only basic services for the tenant. Services such as gas, electricity, water and telephones are installed but separately metered so that tenants pay their own bills for these items. No other services are provided. Units are let on a full insuring and repairing basis and the installation of other services such as heating is the responsibility of the tenant. This approach reduces management involvement and costs.

Basic property services   Services such as heating, lighting, hot and cold water for drinking and washing, maintenance, periodic decoration and waste disposal are provided. These services are offered at the majority of small unit developments as part of the lease or licence.

Office services   In addition to the above services in each unit, many developments offer central office services to their tenants. Provision is often made for a conference room, canteen, reception and display area. Services provided at central reception can include typing/word-processing, mailing, telephone answering, telex, computing and printing.

Business services   Business advice is a valuable service to the small firm. An experienced manager or developer/manager who can offer sound advice will greatly help the tenant's business confidence. He can also act as a signpost to more specialized services. Some schemes offer book-keeping, invoice, payroll and VAT services.

Totally serviced units   The Enterprise Workshop concept provides an example of the totally serviced environment. Workspace is provided fully equipped for particular business activities and the tenant purchases the entire package. Charges can even be made at an hourly rate. These developments are usually marketed on a short-term basis to tenants who wish to try out their new business ideas.

The amount and type of services offered will depend on the individual development and the market to which it is directed.

Canteen, reception and display facilities are useful services to provide because they give a focus and identity to the development as well as providing a point of contact between firms. Running a small business can be a lonely affair and contact with others in a similar situation is often beneficial. The provision of shared services can easily be overdone. Many developers have found that facilities are underused. What may seem vital to one business may be irrelevant to another. Service-oriented businesses such as accountants and management consultants will possess their own office services. As a result they will find central office services less useful than the small manufacturer. The apparent advantage for the small firm in the economies of scale derived from sharing is not always borne out in practice. If in doubt, follow one of two courses of action:

1 Develop services incrementally. Only consider provision when tenants show enough interest to provide adequate demand.
2 Pass on the provision of all but essential services to a tenant, such as a typing agency, specifically attracted for the purpose.

Many of these problems can be minimized by companies who are subdividing, for many services will already be available within their existing company. Additional use of these services may increase their viability and be beneficial to all concerned.

Estimating service charges

Services can be charged on a pro rata basis according to use or at an all-inclusive rate added to the tenants' rental. Services such as photocopying, telex and the use of a conference-room are generally charged according to use. It is harder to distinguish the use each business makes of many other types of services and these are usually apportioned between tenants. Once it has been decided which items will be charged collectively, annual costs for each of these services should be calculated. From this calculation it is possible to derive a cost for providing all communal services. These costs can then be apportioned amongst tenants on the basis of floorspace occupied or simply by dividing total costs by the number of tenants. These average charges per tenant can then be modified to take account of any inconsistencies attributable to the characteristics of individual units. Services must at least pay for themselves. If the cost is greatly in excess of prevailing market prices or uptake is limited, reconsider providing each service rather than reducing charges. This is one area of the cost structure in which local authority developments may consider a subsidy. However, if usage is low it is important to assess why – some services may simply not be needed.

Management and the provision of services

Whichever services are to be provided, there is a range of ways in which they can be managed. Different services may require a different approach. Each is discussed separately.

The provision and management of a reception and inquiry system

If such a facility is provided, its management can be undertaken either by the developer/manager or, as is increasingly popular, by a tenant. The offer of reduced rental to a business or typing agency frequently proves attractive. Services can include typing and an answer-phone service, which can be charged separately. This may well provide a viable level of trade for a new start-up typing agency which undertakes these duties.

Control and security of premises

A policy for control and security will have to be developed and implemented. This will involve a variety of elements including:

1 general property security against vandalism
2 security of occupants' units
3 security of monies including rents and other petty cash.

Additionally, policies about access to buildings, use of car parking, vehicular access and internal access will be needed. Decisions about key holders and hours of opening should also be made. Remember local residents may object to late night users.

A busy, diverse site can both create and solve security problems. The constant comings and goings make it relatively easy for unauthorized people to find their way into premises. On the other hand, a complex in which people are working late and irregularly will be less of an attraction to vandals and thieves than units only occupied from 8.30 am to 5.30 pm. The siting of a reception area near the entrance to a development can solve many day-time security problems. It might be appropriate to consider the use of a security company to oversee premises outside working hours.

Insurance

Insurance will be needed for the main structure, fire risks and third party liability. If slates or bricks fall from your property and injure passing pedestrians or cars, you will be liable. It is worth obtaining several quotations; variations between brokers can be quite large. Insurance premiums for multi-unit property have increased very rapidly in the last two years and it is becoming increasingly difficult to obtain satisfactory cover at reasonable prices.

It is also important to ensure that tenants provide adequate cover for themselves. They should be covered for risks such as the loss of money, equipment, stock and damage caused by burglary. In the case of public liability, tenants are required by the Employer's Liability (Compulsory Insurance) Act 1969 to obtain adequate appropriate insurance cover.

Maintenance and repair

Responsibility for maintenance and repair can be assigned to the tenant as part of the lease or can be retained by the developer. Routine maintenance is best dealt with on a regular prearranged basis and a schedule should be developed to aid the organization of maintenance. If it is not undertaken systematically, maintenance can become a costly, time-consuming activity.

The management of maintenance will need to consider two main issues: the purchase and storage of necessary equipment and the frequency of maintenance tasks themselves.

Storage of equipment and supplies   Day-to-day maintenance will require: tools (spanners, screwdrivers, hammers, ladders, step-ladders, mops, buckets, cloths, etc); equipment (light bulbs and tubes, screws, nails, glue, oil, tap washers).

Careful regulation of the store is essential. 'Borrowed' items are not always returned. Keep a record of what is used so that maintenance costs can be calculated. Monitoring the use of items also allows an objective assessment of what is needed most frequently. This allows efficient purchasing.

Frequency of maintenance tasks Various maintenance activities should be undertaken regularly, but at different intervals. Time periods for some activities are described below:

1 General cleaning, replenishing soap and servicing toilet facilities – *daily*
2 Cleaning of windows, floor maintenance – *three-monthly intervals*
3 Checking and replacement of lights – *three-monthly intervals*
4 Maintenance of lifts – *annually*
5 Servicing of heating system – *annually*
6 Checking roof, gutters etc. and cleaning as appropriate – *annually*
7 Painting (interior and exterior) – *three-yearly intervals*

Enter each of these activities into a maintenance programme to ensure they are undertaken. It is all too easy to forget. Activities can then be undertaken in a controlled way, rather than as an emergency.

Finance for this work can be included in the service charge element of the rent. The work itself can be undertaken by a part-time handyman. Major repairs and maintenance are best dealt with separately. Many developers have a separate fund, financed as part of the service charge, for such eventualities.

Day-to-day caretaking

Routine caretaking will include the daily cleaning of public areas, the cleaning and general servicing of toilets, and the maintenance of lighting systems including emergency lighting if fitted. It will also include the supervision of a waste disposal system. The disposal of waste is a major problem at most small unit developments and if left uncontrolled can rapidly lead to an unsightly working environment. This work can all be undertaken by a part-time caretaker, or as a service by one of the tenants.

Conference area

If a conference area is to be provided it is best to charge on a pro rata basis according to use. The cost of this service should include setting-out and cleaning charges as well as actual time used. It will be necessary to develop a booking system which can be administered on a day-to-day basis.

Display area

Many developers provide some form of display for tenants' products. This will need to be properly managed. Without such control, experience suggests that business can be lost rather than gained by bad presentation.

Canteen facilities

It is valuable to have canteen facilities at a conversion or subdivision scheme. These can be provided by the developer but most developers prefer to delegate this function to a tenant. In this case the developer's concern will rest mainly with usage and appropriate levels of cleanliness. Canteen facilities are well worth consideration as many developers have commented on how they lead to a common spirit amongst tenants. For the company subdividing underused space it may be possible to use the canteen facilities of the existing business.

One problem with canteen facilities is that they sometimes attract a lot of people not associated with a development. They provide a valuable coffee or lunch venue for lorry drivers delivering to the site and other groups. The added security and car (or lorry) parking problems which this can create has led some developers to restrict their use to tenants and their guests only.

Monitoring the development

A vital management function is the monitoring of a project. This will include a more formal review of the financial targets, tenants' success, turnover of tenants, as well as the less formal feedback from tenants themselves. Feedback is very important to the overall development of small units. Tenants' views about the conversion or subdivision and the environment that has been created for them are important. What are the strong and weak points of the development? Monitoring is best undertaken at two levels:

1 **Formal monitoring** This will be based on occupancy levels, rates, turnover, analysis of empty units, rental income, service use and other similar items. It will necessitate the development of a systematic monitoring system which will allow annual assessments to be made. The management system discussed earlier will provide you with most of the information required for formal monitoring. At the end of each year you should assess the performance of the units against your initial appraisal and cashflow analysis. If the development is progressing on target, then there will be little need to take action. If, on the other hand, the performance is not what was anticipated, it will be appropriate to modify aspects of the development.

2 **Informal monitoring** This will be based on the comments of individual tenants arising from day-to-day management of the property. It is useful to keep a notebook handy to record comments so that they can be assessed alongside the more formal review. A suggestion box is sometimes a useful way of picking up comments which tenants might otherwise keep to themselves. It is important to remember that, as landlord, you may have a very different view of how things are developing from your tenants.

Information derived from monitoring should be used to improve the development and create a better working environment for tenants. Contented tenants will stay with you; unhappy tenants will move elsewhere. If you can discover the strengths and benefits for tenants at your development, use these in your advertising when new units become available.

Key points

When developing the management strategy it will be necessary to consider the following key questions:

1 What style of management is appropriate to the development?
2 What management structure should be adopted?
3 What form of contract will be used between landlord and tenant?
4 How will rents and other charges be assessed and collected?
5 What services will be provided and how will they be managed?
6 How will the project be monitored?

Chapter 10

Case Studies

The previous nine chapters have outlined and illustrated the range of issues and approaches which are involved in the conversion and subdivision of property for small business use. Three case studies are presented in this final chapter which show how individual developers have converted and subdivided properties. Although the case studies have been selected because they illustrate many of the specific issues discussed in the book, they also reveal the often idiosyncratic approach taken at many developments.

In the first case study, Otley Mills, West Yorkshire, Ronnie Duncan's conversion has been undertaken in two major stages with little outside financial or other assistance. Frequently frustrated by 'authority', Mr Duncan's development now has approximately 150 people employed in a wide range of enterprises.

Cox, Wilcox and Company, the second case study, illustrates the ease with which small businesses can diversify their activities and become small-scale property developers. For Cox, Wilcox and Company, the subdivision of their property has allowed a planned reduction and eventual stabilization of their existing metal manufacturing business.

The final case study, the Lincoln Innovation Centre, was developed by Lincoln Enterprise Agency to complement the existing counselling service offered to small businesses in Lincoln. This scheme has been undertaken at minimal cost using the benefits of sponsorship and goodwill. It provides an excellent example of the opportunities open to the enterprise agency movement in the provision of small starter units.

Otley Mills

Introduction

Otley Mills provide an example of a development undertaken incrementally as a result of the contraction of William Ackroyd Worsted Spinners Limited. The development began in 1978 when the company managing director, Ronnie Duncan, investigated the possible reuse of buildings which had been redundant for over 60 years. In 1983,

William Ackroyd Limited was placed in receivership. William Ackroyd Holdings was left with all the redundant buildings. The conversion and subdivision was undertaken in two stages: first the creation of the Duncan Craft Workshops and second the development of workshops in Pegholme Mill and other smaller associated buildings.

Otley Mills are located on the former main road to Skipton on the western side of Otley. Nearby there is residential and other industrial property and consequently the general development of the area is mixed. The site slopes steeply down from the main road towards the river Wharfe. The sloping nature of the site has been important to the development. Access to the site on the western side is relatively easy. Access to the eastern side is far less easy. Firstly, the buildings continue up to the edge of the road with consequent parking and obstruction problems, and secondly initial access is down a very steep lane.

The site is bordered at its northern edge by the River Wharfe which in the last century was used to power the spinning machinery. The position of the mill by the river presents problems of flooding from time to time. Parts of the site are claimed as washlands by the Water Authority. Development potential is hence restricted.

The buildings

The buildings which form the basis of this development are made up of three groups. All are multi-storey, one of which is four storeys and has the typical access problems of multi-storey buildings. The buildings themselves were in various states of repair. One of the buildings had not been used for 60 years and another had been very much underutilized as a wool warehouse. The age of some of the buildings is also an important consideration. Pegholme Mill, some 27,000 square feet on three storeys, was in excellent overall condition with an operating sprinkler system. This building had been the production base of Ackroyd Worsted Spinners until 1983.

The oldest mill buildings dated from 1780 and consequently, as one might expect, their condition was not too good. The orientation and nature of the buildings lent themselves very well to conversion, particularly the warehouse which had been used for wool storage and sorting. The buildings were built around a cobbled courtyard and this provided the opportunity for a very effective design for small units.

The process of conversion: Phase 1. Duncan Craft Workshops

Subdivision began in 1978. Ackroyds initially approached a local architect, the Leeds City Planning Department and a local estate agent to discuss the development potential of the buildings for small enterprise workshops. All were sceptical. A major stumbling block was access onto the site from the east from the A660 trunk road. Since the completion of the development Otley has been 'bypassed' by a new road system leaving the former trunk road as a quiet backwater.

To gain reasonable access and an adequate amount of car parking space for the development it was necessary to demolish some of the listed buildings at the site. The planning department was not keen on this proposition and they held back the development for some time whilst the problems were negotiated. Eventually it was agreed that the old mill should be demolished to make way for car parking space; the whole development then became feasible and planning permission was given. In total it took three years to gain approval and complete this phase of the development.

Work undertaken   The basic layouts of the buildings lend themselves well to small enterprise workshops. The internal structure of the warehouse, for example, only needed partitioning to appropriate size units. A great deal of work was needed in basic repair and maintenance because the buildings had not been occupied for 60 years. The state of the roofs of all the buildings was poor, guttering was down and the buildings were in a generally run-down condition. This general maintenance work required a considerable amount of time. Outside contractors were employed to undertake the work and it was done to a high standard. The old listed mill was demolished, the site cleared, the car park laid out with spaces for 40 to 50 cars.

Costings   Some attempt to pre-cost the development was made although it was difficult to do this with any certainty and a 30 percent contingency was added onto the final figure in anticipation of any problems. It is noteworthy that the majority of this 30 percent contingency was used during the course of the conversion. The total cost of the conversion was £55,000; this money rescued the building and put it to productive use. However, because the buildings were listed and would have had to have been maintained in a safe condition anyway, Ackroyds did not see the total cost of the development as £55,000. They discounted maintenance costs which would have been required, and they also discounted the demolition of the old mill and the sale value of the stone, leaving a figure of approximately £36,000 for the total conversion. This provided work opportunity for some 45 people in 12,000 square feet of high standard workshop units. The conversion as a whole cost approximately £3 per square foot.

The units   Initially the intention was for very small units, less than 500 square feet. It became obvious to Mr Duncan as the development progressed, however, that the demand was for various sized units. In general the kind of people that were coming to them were small enterprises employing three, four or five people, rather than the one-man businesses which had been anticipated. Consequently emphasis was placed on larger units than had originally been anticipated and units of 500, 600 and 700 square feet are now minimum sizes offered. The management approach is flexible and units of a variety of sizes are available to fit the needs of individual tenants. The nature of the conversion is such that the basic structural changes are being undertaken by the landlord but internal work is left to the tenants themselves, particularly if any specific needs such as extra lighting or additional fire-proofing are required. The conversion is essentially simple and, unlike some other developments, each individual unit does not have its own services, toilets and the like. These are provided centrally. Separate metering of electricity is found in each of the units and some of them have three-phase electricity installed. None of the units is heated. Heating has to be provided by the tenant on an independent basis.

Phase 2. Pegholme Mill

William Ackroyd Holdings, also owned by Ronnie Duncan, acquired Pegholme Mill in 1983 following the collapse of William Ackroyd Limited, the worsted spinners. Mr Duncan decided to build upon the success of the Duncan Craft Workshop development and convert more small business units.

Work undertaken   The three-storey building was in good condition. Access was sufficient for most prospective users. The building had a goods hoist and goods lift and stone staircases at either end. Subsequently one of these staircases proved too narrow for fire escape purposes and was replaced by a new wooden stair system at a cost of £4,000. The installation of the stairway was relatively simple except for the modification required to the sprinkler system.

Units have been created on either side of a corridor which runs along the centre of each floor of the building. At either end are the staircases. Units are partitioned by plaster boards fixed to a wooden frame. The appearance may not be attractive but it is effective and tenants can decorate or improve units to their own requirements. Originally the partitions were only to a height of eight feet but disturbances from noise and dust necessitated raising these to ceiling level. Each unit is separately metered for electricity. Tenants provide their own heating.

Recently a hot-air heating system has been installed at a cost of £16,000. Whilst this was provided primarily to protect the sprinkler system, tenants can buy heat if they require additional heating in their units.

The subdivision has been undertaken on a piecemeal basis. As tenants have shown interest, then more space has been divided. All the necessary works have been undertaken by a small local jobbing builder.

The units   The units vary in size from 200 square feet to over 1000 square feet. Because the interior finish is left to the tenants, there is considerable variation in the quality of the units. However, most tenants have produced working space of good quality.

Costings   The conversion of Pegholme has cost approximately £90,000 so far. When the final part of the third floor is complete that figure will have risen to £100,000. Major expenditure has arisen because of the installation of the new staircase and heating system. It is notable that no external sources of finance have been used for the development.

Management

The management of the entire site is now undertaken by Ronnie Duncan, the managing director of Ackroyds, from part of the former company's offices. The rest of the office building has been sublet to small service companies without any subdivision work being necessary. Two part-time workers are employed to undertake general site maintenance.

Lettings are based either on formal lease agreements or, in the case of the Duncan Craft Workshops, by written agreement, quarterly in advance. Rents are currently set at £1.50 per square foot for all space regardless of location within the building. Rental income is currently of the order of £65,000 per year, made up of £30,000 from Pegholme, £18,000 from the Craft Workshops and additional rent from the other associated buildings.

No services are provided to tenants other than insurance, which is charged pro rata per square foot, and heating which can be bought pro rata.

The buildings now employ approximately 160 people in a wide variety of activities. The developer has attempted to segregate uses between the two main buildings so as to minimize incompatibility. The craft users, who range from soft-toy manufacturers to woodwind instrument makers, occupy the Craft Workshops. Pegholme Mill and other workspace is occupied by more artisan-type activities such as printers and bookbinders, piano makers and woodworkers. All the tenants sell direct from their workshops, introducing a retail element to the scheme. This diversity is widened by other specifically retail and service-oriented companies. Tenants have not been difficult to attract. Billboards and word of mouth have been the major means of advertising. Turnover of tenants has also been low.

Conclusion

The conversion of Otley Mills illustrates the possibilities of an incremental approach to subdivision which can bring a reasonable rate of return. It demonstrates how this approach minimizes the need for external finance and how a more than satisfactory standard can be achieved at modest cost. The development has not been without its problems. Whilst all developers have few good words to say about the local Planning system, major delays and difficulties were experienced even after initial satisfactory discussions with the local authority. No public finance was available for this development. Whilst the developer approached all the public funding agencies, none was able to help. These problems are best seen as minor difficulties in what is a very successful development.

Ten Acre Works, Birmingham

Introduction

Ten Acre Works is comprised of a number of brick-built Victorian industrial buildings. The site is situated in an area of mixed residential and industrial land on Pershore Road to the south of Birmingham. The site is owned by Cox, Wilcox and Company, metal goods manufacturers. Their subdivision scheme shows how a declining company can avoid failure and survive by diversifying into property development. In 1977 Cox, Wilcox and Company employed 85 workers and exported to many countries all over the world. Since 1977 the company has lost much of its export market and it now only employs 15 workers. Despite this apparent failure in the company's manufacturing activities, it has become a very successful small-scale property development business.

In 1978 Mr Jones, the company's managing director, realized his business was failing and needed to diversify. On business trips to the Far East he visited many of the countries which posed the greatest source of competition for his metal manufacturing business. He recognized that the company was unable to compete with these low-wage and highly mechanized producers. On the basis of what he found and with the realization that within the foreseeable future his trading situation could only worsen, he decided that he must act quickly. He reduced the number of manufactured products and much to his regret made severe reductions in the size of the workforce. Despite all his best efforts to compete more effectively, his company's market position and profit margins continued their ever downward spiral. Having used the majority of surplus funds to keep the company trading, he realized that the only remaining asset was the factory which the company owned. Although he had no experience of property development, he decided that the only way of saving the company was to diversify and somehow make use of the 29,000 square feet single-storey building.

The company's reduction in output and smaller workforce meant that large, but dispersed, areas of the factory were unused. He therefore decided to consolidate the company's machinery into a smaller area of the factory. Mr Jones knew that concentration of production in a small area could help to reduce the company's heating and lighting costs; this could not be achieved when the unused areas were dispersed throughout the factory. Although these savings were beneficial, he realised that the major costs were rates, insurance and maintenance. He decided that the only way to avoid these and gain income from the property was to subdivide the premises into small business units. Rates and insurance would then be paid by the tenants, and maintenance costs overcome by including a clause in each lease about tenants maintaining all units to a reasonable standard. The rental income from the subdivided units would ensure that previously unused areas of the factory were once again providing a financial contribution to the company.

Mr Jones had hoped the funds generated from renting the vacant floorspace could be used to finance the future expansion of the company. In the event, the company has been further affected by the general decline in the metal goods industry. But whilst many of his previous competitors and friends have gone out of business, he has been able to survive by expanding the property development side of his business as the manufacturing area has declined.

The subdivision process

Since Mr Jones had no previous experience of property development or subdivision, he contacted a variety of groups to discuss his ideas. These included friends in the property business, architects and building and planning officers. Eventually a plan for the subdivision of the whole site was drawn up. This served a dual purpose. Firstly, it defined the areas which could most easily be subdivided into new units. Secondly, it gave the company a structured but flexible route for further contraction. This ensured the company did not suffer financially from having underutilized space, because as soon as an area became unused the company reconsolidated its position in the factory along the lines of the predetermined plan.

All machinery was moved by the company's own employees during weekends and at other times when production was slack. This ensured that the company's normal production was not affected by these activities. Some of the employees were also involved in installing new electricity meters and power points to the new units.

In the first phase of the development four units were created. These units were subdivided by breeze-block walls. All metal girders were enclosed to ensure fire regulation requirements were achieved. Entrances to the units were provided by installing ordinary household garage doors. The units have an average size of 2000 square feet and are fully self-contained with their own office and toilet facilities. Access to each of these units was provided by a narrow passageway. Problems with this restricted access route and a lack of nearby car parking space for the new tenants was overcome when Mr Jones bought two houses adjoining the factory. The gardens to the rear of these houses were about 200 feet long and ran parallel to the passageway. After reducing the size of the gardens to only 20 feet, the remaining area provided improved access to the units and additional car parking spaces. Permission to do this was at first refused by Birmingham City Council, but after negotiations they eventually allowed the development to proceed. The houses themselves were improved and refurbished and they are also rented to tenants. The subdivision process took a total of 18 months to complete.

The cost of the subdivision was about £6.41 per square foot, but this does include the purchase of the two houses and rewiring work which would probably have been necessary anyway. Finance for the subdivision came from company funds and a bank loan.

Despite the company's efforts to remain competitive, their trading position worsened. As a result, they decided to contract further and develop three more units of about 2000 square feet. The way in which these units were developed provides a contrast to the previous phase of the development because they were subdivided at practically no cost to the company. They demonstrate how easily and cheaply subdivision can be undertaken. Partitions to divide the units were not constructed; instead existing walls within the factory were used to subdivide the units. No additional facilities were provided and the tenants in these three units share washing and toilet facilities with Cox, Wilcox and Company. Separate access routes to these units could not be provided and tenants share an entrance to the building. Although this is a little inconvenient at times, all the companies concerned seem happy with the situation.

All tenancies are managed by Mr Jones who is available on site at all times. Tenants in the four self-contained units which were completed in the first phase of the development have three-year leases. These require all repairs to be carried out by the tenants and stipulate that interior redecoration and exterior painting is undertaken every three years. All of these tenants had an initial 18-month rental period at £1 per square foot to enable them to carry out alterations to their units. After this, rents rose to £2 per square foot. The remaining units, which share access and other facilities with Cox, Wilcox and Company, do not have formal leases. Instead they have a 'gentlemen's agreement'. Due to the inconvenience of sharing facilities they have rental levels of about £1.20 per square foot. Tenants in these units also share some services with the owner, whereas other units have separately metered and billed services. Insurance and rates on the building are paid for by the owner. Tenants' contributions to this are determined by the proportion of square footage occupied. All tenants have their own insurance against theft, damage and loss of trade.

Mr Jones strongly believes that it is important to develop a good relationship with tenants, so that difficulties and differences can be resolved more amicably. Despite this, there have been some problems with tenants. The most notable of these was when one of the tenants became bankrupt and there were considerable problems in repossessing the unit from the liquidators. Eventually the matter had to be resolved in court. With hindsight Mr Jones believes he should have stuck more strongly to the clause in his leases which allows immediate repossession of property if rents become more than one month overdue.

Conclusion

The enterprise which Mr Jones has shown in diversifying his company's activities demonstrates how a failing business can once again become successful by subdividing its property. The company's diversification into property development by subdividing its one remaining asset, the factory, has been extremely successful and ensured the survival and prosperity of the business. The new companies which have moved into the subdivided units produce a diverse range of products and now employ over 100 people. Mr Jones's method of diversifying his company's activities could serve as an example to many other struggling companies of how they can once again become profitable and successful.

Lincoln Innovation Centre

Introduction

The Lincoln Innovation Centre is being developed by Lincoln Enterprise Agency to provide small unit accommodation for new start-up companies. Innovation Centre is perhaps a misnomer as the centre is intended not specifically for the development of innovations. Initial plans for the centre were drawn up in early 1985. It was originally intended to have tenants operating in the units in September 1985. However, this date slowly slipped back so that tenants finally came into the building in June 1986.

Lincoln Enterprise Agency was aware from its general counselling role that many small start-up businesses in Lincoln were having problems in finding suitable premises. Like many other parts of the country, low cost accommodation was at a premium. Because this shortage was impeding the development of potential companies, the agency decided to act. Not only did the agency have a very clear understanding of the market for small units, but in several cases it already had potential tenants in mind. A considerable amount of uncertainty was consequently removed. The underlying philosophy of the development reflected the agency's aims to help small businesses in the early stages of their life by careful counselling and advice.

The building

The search for a building was limited because a suitable property was offered to the agency by British Rail on favourable terms. The Executive Director of the agency was a former Area Manager with British Rail. He was aware that the Board had surplus property and knew the right people to contact. He was consequently able to expedite a search for surplus buildings which the Board might make available. As British Rail are equally committed to community support schemes, a building was quickly identified and made available to the agency. The agreement to take over the building at a peppercorn rent was made at one short site meeting. An understanding of the red tape and personal acquaintance with the negotiating parties was very useful.

The building was a former railwaymen's mess room. It is a long, narrow two-storey building of approximately 3000 square feet, flanked by railway track. It is light and airy, having windows on all sides. The building had two entrances and internal staircases at either end making access very easy. It was also well supplied with toilets and wash basins. The size and configuration of the building made it ideal for the agency's requirements. Another major advantage for the scheme was the agreement reached with British Rail for the letting of the property. It is let at a nominal rental on a six-monthly renewable agreement, with an initial agreement for a period of three years. This latter point was vital if Community Programme workers were to become involved in the development work. The relatively short-term letting agreement could in theory prove a problem, although repossession by British Rail after three years is most unlikely.

The conversion process

The initial layout and plans for the conversion were undertaken by an architect engaged by the agency. He worked on a time basis (payment on an hourly basis) to keep costs to a minimum. Early in the discussions with the architect it was decided that the best approach would be to divide the building into two, halfway along its length, with a fire-resistant breeze-block wall. Access could then be gained to each half of the building via one of the existing stairways. Eleven units of between 100 and 350 square feet have been created simply by partitioning across the width of the building and providing short corridors for access to some units. Fire regulations stipulated that the staircases at either end of the building should be accessible in the event of a fire. To enable this alternative means of escape, a fire door was built in the central dividing wall of the building. Keys are contained in breakable glass cases by the door. This may prove a problem to tenants in the future because it allows access to units, and is a possible security risk, but it was the only way adequate means of escape could be achieved without building a corridor along one side of the building and reducing the available lettable space.

The existing toilet facilities were removed; this allowed space for one of the units. A new toilet area was created which is more appropriate for the new users of the building. Every advantage was made of the many windows on all elevations to provide each of the units with high levels of natural light.

Although the building was structurally sound and had only been vacated a short period before the agency took it over, some major maintenance work was necessary. The building's flat roof was in need of repair. British Rail had also condemned the electrical wiring and this had to be replaced.

The agency costed this work out in some detail, as is seen in Table 10.1 taken from their feasibility study. These costs were then translated into the cashflow projection in Table 10.2. It is noteworthy that the figures in the cashflow projection show an overall

Table 10.1   Lincoln Innovation Centre: feasibility study

Complete rewiring, adequate power points etc.	£1500)	Complete rewiring including	
Central heating servicing	£300) or	provision for heating	£3000
Gas reconnection	£1200)		
Provision of partitions	£1000		
Roof repairs	£1100 (includes labour)		
General repairs	£1700		
Decoration to minimum standards	£500		
	£7300		

increase of £6000 on the original estimates. No labour charges were included in the costings. The development used Community Programme labour for all work other than roof repairs, for which appropriate labour was not available. Major labour costs were consequently eliminated. Funds for materials and other works were provided by a range of sponsors including Lincoln City Council. The use of Community Programme workers was not without its problems. The Programme requires any development work to have a long-term benefit, which necessitated the negotiation of the initial three-year agreement for the property with British Rail. The work also required the approval of local unions. This was at first a sticking point. British Rail are funding some of the external environmental works as part of their drive to improve the railway's image.

Management

The units are being separately managed from the agency by a part-time agency director who undertakes the full day-to-day operation and supervision of the development. He also gives advice and support to the users. Rentals are charged at the rate of £10 per month regardless of size. The units are let on a licence, the text of which is given in Appendix 13. The licence agreement provides an easy access or exit tenancy for a period of up to one year. After that time, assuming they are still in business and on a firm footing, the agency will help companies find a more suitable

Table 10.2 Lincoln Innovation Centre: cashflow projection

Item	Month 6 Sept 85	7 Oct 85	8 Nov 85	9 Dec 85	10 Jan 86	11 Feb 86	12 Mar 86	Total
Manager/Assistant Director's Salary	300	300	300	300	300	300	300	2,100
Heating	200	300	300	300	500	500	500	2,600
Lighting	80	80	150	140	150	180	170	950
Rates	750	—	—	—	—	—	750	1,500
Insurance	200	—	—	—	—	—	—	200
Materials	4,000	4,600	4,000	500	100	100	—	13,300
Cleaning/Security	50	50	50	50	50	50	50	350
Total	£5,580	£5,330	£4,800	£1,290	£1,100	£1,130	£1,770	£21,000

NOTE: Telephone, postage, stationery and sundry items included in Lincoln Enterprise Agency cashflow.

base. It is not the intention that the centre will become the permanent location for companies. Whilst the system works well at present, it remains to be seen whether the licence will encourage tenants to be moved on after their initial period.

Conclusion

Lincoln Innovation Centre is very new and it has had teething problems in getting established. It does, though, illustrate the way in which enterprise agencies can get workshop developments off the ground at very low cost and make a major contribution to the provision of premises for new start-up businesses.

Appendix 1

Miscellaneous Addresses

British Technology Group
101 Newington Causeway
London SE1 6BU
01 403 6666

British Technology Group North
9 Hunters Mews
Wilmslow
Cheshire SK9 2AR
0625 532343

British Technology Group Scotland
87 St Vincent Street
Glasgow G2 5TF
041 221 1820

Business in the Community
227a City Road
London EC1V 1LX
01 253 3716

Investors in Industry PLC
91 Waterloo Road
London SE1 8XP
01 928 7822

Local Enterprise Development Unit (LEDU)
LEDU House
Upper Galwally
Belfast BT8 4TB
0232 691031

Scottish Development Agency
120 Bothwell Street
Glasgow G2 7JP
041 248 2700

Scottish Office
New St Andrew's House
St James' Centre
Edinburgh
Lothian EH1 3SX
031 556 8400

Welsh Development Agency
Treforest Industrial Estate
Pontypridd
Mid Glam CF37 5UT
044 385 2666

Appendix 2

Locations and Contact Addresses for Enterprise Zones

Belfast
Belfast Enterprise Zone Office
Adelaide Street
Belfast BT2 8NR
0232 248449

Clydebank
Development Officer
Clydebank Task Force
Clyde House
170 Kilbowie Road
Clydebank G81 2DR
041 952 0084

Corby
Director of Industry
Corby Industrial Development Centre
Douglas House
Queens Square
Corby
Northants NN17 1PL
05366 62571

Delyn
Delyn Borough Council
Enterprise House
Aber Park
Flint
Clwyd CH6 5BD
03526 4004

Dudley
Industrial Development Unit
Council House
Dudley
West Midlands DY1 1HF
0384 55433

Glanford
Glanford Borough Council
Council Offices
Station Road
Brigg
South Humberside DN20 8EG
0652 52441

Hartlepool
Industrial Development Officer
Civic Centre
Hartlepool
Cleveland TS24 8AY
0429 66522

Invergordon
Invergordon Enterprise Zone Office
62 High Street
Invergordon IV18 0DH
0349 853666

Isle of Dogs
London Dockland's Development
  Corporation
West India House
Millwall Dock
London E14 9TJ
01 515 3000

Londonderry
Londonderry Enterprise Zone Office
3 Water Street
Londonderry BT48 6HN
0504 263992

Lower Swansea Valley
Director of Planning
Swansea City Council
Guildhall
Swansea SA1 4NL
0792 50821

Middlesbrough
Enterprise Zone Office
Vancouver House
Gurney Street
Middlesbrough
Cleveland TS1 1QP
0642 222279

Milford Haven
Preseli District Council
Cambria House
PO Box 27
Haverfordwest
Dyfed SA61 1TP
0437 4551

North East Lancashire
NE Lancs Development Association
Stephen House
Bethesda Street
Burnley
Lancashire BB11 1PR
0282 37411

North West Kent
NW Kent Enterprise Office
Mountbatten House
3 Military Road
Chatham
Kent ME4 4JE
0634 826233

Rotherham
Rotherham Metropolitan District Council
Department of Planning
Norfolk House
Walker Place
Rotherham
South Yorkshire S60 1QT
0709 72099

Salford
Industrial Liaison Officer
City of Salford
Civic Centre
Chorley Road
Swinton
Greater Manchester M27 2AD
061 793 3237

Trafford
Industrial Development Officer
Trafford Metropolitan Borough Council
Town Hall
Stretford
Greater Manchester M32 0TH
061 872 2101

Scunthorpe
Civic Centre
Ashby Road
Scunthorpe
South Humberside DN16 1AB
0724 862141

Speke
Senior Assistant Secretary
City Solicitors Department
Liverpool City Council
Room 201
Municipal Buildings
Dale Street
Liverpool L69 2DH
051 227 3911

Tayside
Director of Planning
Angus District Council
County Buildings
Forfar DD8 3LG
0307 65101

Telford
Enterprise Zone Manager
Telford Development Corporation
Priorslee Hall
Priorslee
Telford
Shropshire TF2 9NT
0952 613131

Tyneside
Central Policy Division
City of Newcastle upon Tyne
Civic Centre
Newcastle upon Tyne NE99 2BH
0632 328520

Gateshead Metropolitan Borough Council
Town Hall
Gateshead
Tyne & Wear NE8 1BP
0632 771011

Wakefield
Planning Department
City of Wakefield District Council
Newton Bar
Wakefield
West Yorkshire WF1 2TT
0924 370211

Wellingborough
Director of Development
Wellingborough Borough Council
Council Offices
Tithe Barn Road
Wellingborough
Northants NN8 1BN
0933 229777

Workington
Enterprise Zone Manager
Allerdale District Council
Holmewood
Cockermouth
Cumbria CA13 0DW
0900 65656

Appendix 3

Planning Circulars

Circular 22/80 'Development Control Policy and Practice' – general guidelines to planning authorities and developers on how planning applications should be considered

Circular 16/84 'Industrial Development' – especially important re multi-use and special planning characteristics of High Technology industries

Circular 14/85 'Development and Employment' – basic restatement of the presumption in favour of granting permission

Circular 2/86 'Development by Small Business' – clarifies position of small business and the need for a flexible approach

Circular 23/77 'Historic Buildings and Conservation Areas – Policy and Procedure'

Circular 1/85 'The Use of Conditions in Planning Permissions' – gives very useful background on power to impose conditions and the tests of legality, reasonableness, etc.

Appendix 4

CoSIRA Offices

National Headquarters and Wiltshire Office
141 Castle Street
Salisbury
Wiltshire SP1 3TP
0722 336255

County Offices
209 Redland Road
Bristol
Avon BS6 6XU
0272 733433

Agriculture House
55 Goldington Road
Bedford
Beds MK40 3LU
0234 61381

24 Brooklands Avenue
Cambridge
Cambs CB2 2BU
0223 354505

6 Shropshire Street
Audlem
Cheshire CW3 0DY
0270 812012

Highshore House
New Bridge Street
Truro
Cornwall TR1 1AA
0872 73531

Ullswater Road
Penrith
Cumbria CA1 7EH
0768 68752

Agricola House
Church Street
Wirksworth
Derbyshire DE4 4EY
062 982 4848

27 Victoria Park Road
Exeter
Devon EX2 4NT
0392 52616

Room 12/13 Wing D
Government Buildings
Prince of Wales Road
Dorchester
Dorset DT1 1QJ
0305 68558

Morton Road
Darlington
Co Durham DL1 4PT
0325 487123

Sussex House
212 High Street
Lewes
East Sussex BN7 2NH
0273 471339

BEES Small Business Centre
Hay Lane
Braintree
Essex CM7 6ST
0376 47623

Northgate Place
Staple Gardens
Winchester
Hants SO23 8SR
0962 54747

14 Market Place
Howden
Goole
Humberside DN14 7BJ
0430 31138

6–7 Town Lane
Newport
Isle of Wight P030 1JU
0983 528019

8 Romney Place
Maidstone
Kent ME15 6LE
0622 65222

15 Victoria Road
Fulwood
Preston
Lancs PR2 4PS
0772 713038

Council Offices
Eastgate
Sleaford
Lincs NG34 7EB
0529 303241

13 Unthank Road
Norwich
Norfolk NR2 2PA
0603 624498

Hunsbury Hill Farm
Rothersthorpe Road
Northampton
Northants NN4 9QX
0604 65874

William House
Shipton Road
Skelton
York YO3 6WZ
0904 646866

Northumberland Business Centre
Southgate
Morpeth
Northumberland NE61 2EH
0670 58807

Chancel House
East Street
Bingham
Notts NG13 8DR
0949 39222

The Maltings
St John's Road
Wallingford
Oxon OX10 9BZ
0491 35523

Strickland House
The Lawns
Park Street
Telford
Shropshire TF1 3BX
0952 47161

1 The Crescent
Taunton
Somerset TA1 4EA
0823 76905

12 Churchfields Court
Barnsley
South Yorkshire S70 2JT
0226 204367

Bridge Street
Hadleigh
Nr Ipswich
Suffolk IP7 6BY
0473 827893

2 Jenner Road
Guildford
Surrey GU1 3PN
0483 38385

The Abbotsford
10 Market Place
Warwick
Warwickshire CV34 4SL
0926 499593

32 Church Street
Malvern
Worcs WR14 2AZ
068 45 64506

Appendix 5

Development and Intermediate Areas in the UK

Development Areas

England
North West: Liverpool, Widnes & Runcorn, Wigan & St Helens, Wirral & Chester, Workington.

North East: Bishop Auckland, Hartlepool, Middlesbrough, Newcastle upon Tyne, South Tyneside, Stockton-on-Tees, Sunderland.

Yorkshire & Humberside: Rotherham & Mexborough, Scunthorpe, Whitby.

East Midlands: Corby.

South West: Falmouth, Helston, Newquay, Penzance & St Ives, Redruth & Camborne.

Scotland
Arbroath, Bathgate, Cumnock & Sanquhar, Dumbarton, Dundee, Glasgow Greenock, Irvine, Kilmarnock, Lanarkshire.

Wales
Aberdare, Cardigan, Ebbw Vale & Abergavenny, Flint & Rhyl, Holyhead, Lampeter & Aberaeron, Merthyr & Rhymney, Neath & Port Talbot, Pontypridd & Rhondda, South Pembrokeshire, Wrexham.

Intermediate Areas

England
North West: Accrington & Rossendale, Blackburn, Bolton & Bury, part of Manchester, Oldham, Rochdale.

North East:
Darlington, Durham, Morpeth & Ashington.

Yorkshire & Humberside: Barnsley, Bradford, Doncaster, Grimsby, Hull, Sheffield.

West Midlands:
Birmingham, Coventry & Hinckley, Dudley & Sandwell, Kidderminster, Telford & Bridgnorth, Walsall, Wolverhampton.

East Midlands:
Gainsborough.

South West:
Bodmin & Liskeard, Bude, Cinderford & Ross-on-Wye, Plymouth.

Scotland
Ayr, Alloa, Badenoch, Campbeltown, Dunfermline, Dunoon & Bute, Falkirk, Forres, Girvan, Invergordon & Dingwall, Kirkcaldy, Lochaber, Newton Stewart, Skye & Wester Ross, Stewartry, Stranraer, Sutherland, Western Isles, Wick.

Wales
Bangor & Caernarfon, Bridgend, Cardiff, Fishguard, Haverfordwest, Llanelli, Newport, Pontypool & Cwmbran, Porthmadoc & Ffestiniog, Pwllheli, Swansea.

Appendix 6

Regional Offices of the Department of Trade and Industry

Birmingham
Ladywood House
Stephenson Street
Birmingham B2 4DT
021 632 4111

Bristol
The Pithay
Bristol
Avon BS1 2NQ
0272 272666

Leeds
Priestly House
Park Row
Leeds LS1 5SF
0532 443171

London
Charles House
375 Kensington High Street
London W14 8QM
01 603 2060

Manchester
Sunley Building
Piccadilly Plaza
Manchester M1 4BA
061 236 2171

Newcastle
Stonegate House
2 Groat Market
Newcastle upon Tyne NE1 1YN
0632 324722

Nottingham
Severns House
20 Middle Pavement
Nottingham
Notts NG1 7DW
0602 56181

Appendix 7

Regional Offices of the Department of the Environment

Eastern
Charles House
375 Kensington High Street
London W14 8QH
01 603 3444

East Midlands
Cranbrook House
Cranbrook Street
Nottingham NG1 1EY
0602 46121

North West
Sunley Buildings
Piccadilly Plaza
Manchester M1 4BE
061 832 9111

Northern
Wellbar House
Gallowgate
Newcastle upon Tyne
NE1 4TD
0632 327575

South East
Charles House
375 Kensington High Street
London W14 8QH
01 603 3444

South West
Froomsgate House
Rupert Street
Bristol BS1 2ON
0272 297201

West Midlands
Five Ways Tower
Frederick Road
Edgbaston
Birmingham B15 1SJ
021 643 8191

Yorkshire & Humberside
City House
Leeds LS1 4JD
0532 38232

Appendix 8

Business Improvement Services, Contact Addresses

East Midlands Region
Department of Trade and Industry
Severns House
20 Middle Pavement
Nottingham NG1 7DW
0602 506181

Merseyside Sub-Office
Department of Trade and Industry
Graeme House
Derby Square
Liverpool L2 7UP
051 227 4111

North Eastern Region
Department of Trade and Industry
Stanegate House
2 Groat Market
Newcastle upon Tyne NE1 1YN
0632 324722

North Western Region
Department of Trade and Industry
Sunley Building
Piccadilly Plaza
Manchester M1 4BA
061 236 2171

Northern Ireland
Research and Development Branch
Industrial Development Board
IDB House
64 Chichester Street
Belfast BT1 4JX
0232 233233

Scotland
Industry Department for Scotland
Alhambra House
45 Waterloo Street
Glasgow G2 6AT
041 248 2855

Wales
Welsh Office
Industry Department
New Crown Building
Cathays Park
Cardiff CF1 3NQ
0222 823674/824242/824053

Yorkshire & Humberside Region
Department of Trade and Industry
Priestley House
Park Row
Leeds LS1 5LF
0532 443171

Appendix 9

European Coal and Steel Community, Contact Addresses

England
Department of Trade and Industry
Regional Support, Inward Investment and Tourism Division
Kingsgate House
66/74 Victoria Street
London SW1E 6SJ
01 212 0814

Scotland
Industry Department for Scotland
Alhambra House
45 Waterloo Street
Glasgow G2 6AT
041 248 2855

Wales
Investment Department
Welsh Development Agency
Pearl House
Greyfriars Road
Cardiff CF1 3XF
0222 32955

Appendix 10

Areas Eligible for Grants and Loans under the Inner Urban Areas Act 1978

Partnership Areas
Birmingham, Hackney, Islington, Lambeth, Liverpool, Manchester/Salford, Newcastle/Gateshead.

Programme Authorities
Blackburn, Bolton, Bradford, Brent, Coventry, Hammersmith and Fulham, Kingston upon Hull, Knowsley, Leeds, Leicester, Middlesbrough, North Tyneside, Nottingham, Oldham, Rochdale, Sandwell, Sheffield, South Tyneside, Sunderland, Tower Hamlets, Wandsworth, Wirral, Wolverhampton.

Other Districts where UDG bids can be made
Barnsley, Burnley, Doncaster, Ealing, Greenwich, Harringay, Hartlepool, Langbaurgh, Lewisham, Newham, Rotherham, St Helens, Sefton, Southwark, Walsall, Wigan.

Appendix 11

English Estates Offices

Head Office
St George's House
Kingsway
Team Valley
Gateshead
Tyne & Wear NE11 ONA
091–48 78941

Bodmin
53 Fore Street
Bodmin
Cornwall PL31 2JB
0208 3631

Doncaster
Hallgate House
19 Hallgate
Doncaster
S Yorkshire DN1 3NN
0302 66865

Liverpool
Sandon House
157 Regent Road
Liverpool L5 9TF
051 933 2020

Thornaby
Forster House
Allensway
Thornaby
Cleveland TS17 9HA
0642 765911

Workington
Salterbeck Industrial Estate
Workington
Cumbria CA14 5DX
0946 830469

Appendix 12

NCB Enterprise Ltd, Offices

Scotland
Greenpark
Greenend
Liberton
Edinburgh EH17 7PZ
031 664 1461

North East
Coal House
Team Valley
Gateshead
Tyne and Wear NE11 0JD
091 4878822

North Yorkshire
PO Box 13
Allerton Bywater
Castleford WF1C 2AL
0977 556511

Doncaster
St George's
Thorn Road
Doncaster DN1 2JS
0302 66733

Barnsley
Grimethorpe
Nr Barnsley S72 7AB
0226 710000

South Yorkshire
Wath upon Dearne
Nr Rotherham S63 7EW
0709 873331

Western
Staffordshire House
Berry Hill Road
Fenton
Stoke-on-Trent ST4 2NH
0782 48201

North Derbyshire
Bolsover
Nr Chesterfield S44 6AA
0246 822231

North Nottinghamshire
Edwinstowe
Mansfield
Nottinghamshire NG21 9PR
0623 822481

South Nottinghamshire
Bestwood
Nottingham NG6 8UE
0602 273711

South Midlands
Coleorton Hall
Coleorton
Leicester LE6 4FA
0533 413131

South Wales
Coal House
Llanishen
Cardiff CF4 5YS
0222 753232

Kent
1/3 Waterloo Crescent
Dover
0304 201401

Appendix 13

Licence Used at Lincoln Innovation Centre

Licence

1 *During the period of the Licence hereby granted, the Licensee shall remain in occupancy of the premises and will not be entitled to assign any right pursuant to the Licence granted* nor to part with occupation or possession of the premises or any part thereof nor to grant any sub-licence of the whole or any part thereof.

2 *The Licence hereby granted will be terminated by either party giving to the other not less than one month prior notice in writing* from the first day of any month, terminating the Licence on a date therein mentioned. The Licence hereby granted may be terminated forthwith by the Company if, in the Company's opinion, the Licensee is in breach of any of the conditions hereof or any conditions, regulations or requirements applying from time to time to the Licensee's occupancy of the premises.

The Company shall be entitled to exercise such power notwithstanding any time given to the Licensee or any delay in the Company deciding to do so.

The Company shall also be entitled to terminate the Licence forthwith on the Licensee becoming bankrupt or if the Licensee is a Company, in the event of Petition being lodged or a resolution being passed in connection with the winding up of the Company or a Receiver being appointed to all or part of the assets thereof.

3 The Company shall be entitled at any time and from time to time on giving not less than one month's notice to increase the monthly Licence fee payable hereunder. *The Licence fee payable from time to time shall be paid monthly in advance by standing order* on the first day of each calendar month. Any failure to pay the Licence fee on the date due shall entitle the Company to terminate the Licence forthwith. *On signing the Licence to occupy, the Licensee shall deposit with the Company a sum equal to one month's Licence fee.* Said deposit shall be retained by the Company and the balance of same remaining after deduction of any sums due to the Company reimbursed to the Licensee after termination of the Licence to occupy and removal by the Licensee from the premises. The Licensee shall also pay in full the cost of all rechargeable modifications to the unit(s) prior to entry.

4 *The Licensee hereby agrees and undertakes as follows :-*

a) If the Licensee is an individual, he will be personally present and responsible for the premises as an on-site manager. Alternatively he will notify the Company in writing of a deputy who is solely empowered to manage the premises and reach agreements on the Licensee's behalf. If the Licensee is a limited company, partnership or some other form of organisation, a responsible representative of same must be appointed in writing as authorised manager, and such manager will accept personal responsibility for the Licensee's obligations hereunder.

b) *To keep the premises clean, tidy and free from fire or health hazard* and to remove all waste and refuse from the premises daily.

c) To conform at his own expense with all statutory and other regulations pertaining to the Licensee's occupancy or use of the premises and to indemnify the Company against any claim arising from breach of the same. The Licensee will be solely responsible for the safety and maintenance of the premises and all equipment and all processes carried out therein, and for all obligations under the Factory Act, 1961 (as amended) and the Health & Safety at Work Act, 1974 and all subsequent legislation or regulations affecting the health or safety of the Licensee, its employees or visitors to the premises from time to time. *To maintain at least one suitable and serviceable fire extinguisher in the unit(s).*

d) To maintain the premises (excluding responsibility for fair wear and tear to the exterior of the buildings comprised in the same) and the fittings and fixtures and all glass in and upon same in their condition as at commencement of the Licence to occupy. The Licensee will be responsible for all internal repairs and renewals to the Company's satisfaction. Without prejudice to the foregoing, the Licensee will advise the Company forthwith of any damage or deterioration to the premises howsoever arising.

e) To accept any responsibility for and act properly in respect of the use by the Licensee and its employees of the common parts of the building and grounds relative to the premises and surrounding area.

f) *To observe all requirements* and regulations made from time to time by the Company with regard to the use of the premises, the buildings, electricity loading specifications, approach roads and grounds surrounding same including without prejudice to the foregoing generality matters *affecting the security thereof, safety, cleanliness and noise conditions affecting same, car parking, access and loading requirement* and others.

g) *Not to cause or permit to be caused any congestion of the roadways or footpaths.* The Company will have no liability or responsibility for any loss or damage to any vehicles, motor bikes or bicycles parked on or around the premises.

h) To pay for all local rates and all electricity, telephone and other charges or that proportion agreed in respect of the premises and the use thereof and any special insurance risk premium arising from the Licensee's particular use of the premises forthwith upon receipt of an account from the authority or other party to whom any of the said charges are payable. A Statement of Account signed by an authorised representative of the Company shall be conclusive evidence that the sum stated therein is payable by the Licensee. Failure to pay any Account within fourteen days will entitle the Company to terminate the Licence forthwith.

i) *To insure to the Company's satisfaction the Licensee's own effects and business risks* (including obligations as Licensee of the Premises) and to indemnify the Company against third party, public and employer's liability relating to the premises and the Licensee's use thereof. The Licensee will exhibit the relevant Policies and Assurance when called upon to do so by the Company.

j) *Not to undertake any building work nor to erect partitions of any description in the premises nor to modify or alter same in any manner or way without the Company's prior written consent.*

k) On vacating the premises to leave same clean, tidy and in a condition no worse than at date of commencement of the Licence.

l) To permit the Company and any other person authorised by the Company to enter the premises at all reasonable times.

m) *To notify the Company and obtain approval in writing for any proposed installation of machinery or processes which conceivably could have an adverse effect on the premises or the environment with particular regard to pollution, noise, vibration, floor loading and fire hazard etc.*

5 *The Company hereby agrees and undertakes to accept responsibility for repairs to and decoration of the interior common parts of the buildings comprised in the premises required as a result of normal fair wear and tear, and for cleaning and maintenance of the common parts of the subjects of which the premises form part and for fire and public liability insurance to the subjects of which the premises form part taken as a whole (but excluding the matters referred to above) and the costs of lighting in the common parts of the subjects of which the premises form part.*

The level of provision of these facilities will be solely within the control of the Company and will be reviewed by the Company from time to time after prior consultation with the affected Licensees.

6 IT IS HEREBY AGREED AND DECLARED that the Company shall have no liability whatsoever to the Licensee for and the Licensee will indemnify the Company against:-

a) any loss, damage or injury to the Licensee, the Licensee's property or the property or person of any invitees of the Licensee in any respect including any failure or inadequacy in the supply of lighting, power, heating or plumbing installations to the premises or to the common parts of the subjects of which the premises form part; and

b) any damage to the Licensee's goods or any disruption of the Licensee's business as a result of any fire, water damage or other cause.

The Company will have no liability whatsoever for consequential loss or damage howsoever arising.

7 It is hereby agreed and declared that the authorised manager who signs the Licence on behalf of the Licensee will not be released from his obligations without the agreement of the Company in writing to the nominated successor.

8 In addition to the foregoing it is hereby agreed that:-

a) standing orders relating to the operation of the Innovation Centre and displayed at that Location will be adhered to.

b) the premises will not be used for storage purposes.

c) the premises will only be occupied during the normal hours of the business.

Type of Business
or Specific
Conditions

Lincoln Enterprise Agency

LICENCE AGREEMENT IN WITNESS WHEREOF these presents are executed as follows:-

This Licence Agreement is made between Lincoln Enterprise Agency whose registered office is at 10 Park Street, Lincoln (hereinafter called "the Company") and

(BLOCK CAPITALS)	Address ....
on the day of	....
nineteen hundred and	....
	....
(Signed)	Telephone No. ....

(hereinafter called "the Licensee").

They are signed for and on behalf of the COMPANY by	WITNESS
(BLOCK CAPITALS)	(Signed) ....
on the day of	Address ....
nineteen hundred and	....
	....
(Signed)	....

IT IS HEREBY AGREED AS FOLLOWS:-
The Company hereby grants to the Licensee the right to occupy and use the premises known as

Unit No.	for the sole purpose of	starting on
		/ /

until the Licence to occupy is terminated in accordance with the aftermentioned provisions.
Such Licence to occupy is subject to the terms and conditions hereinafter set out.

The Licence fee initially payable by the Licensee, excluding/including general rates, shall be

Subject to review under clause 3 after 12 months.

Appendix 14

Application Form for Prospective Tenant

Application for a Business Unit at

_____

1 Name of applicant ....
   Address ....
   ....
   Telephone ....

2 If already in business:
   Business name ....
   Buiness address ....
   ....
   Telephone ....

3 If a new business:
   (a) Is business: 'sole trader'/'partnership'/limited company?
   Please delete as appropriate.
   (b) How many people will you employ?
   Initially   After 6/12/18 months

4 Nature of business to be conducted in unit:
   Describe processes to be carried on and the end-product where applicable. Type of
   plant/machinery to be installed. State special requirements if any, e.g. chemicals,
   spraying, dust, noise etc.

5 What is the nature, volume and proposed means of disposal of trade refuse or
   effluent?

6 Please give brief details of knowledge/experience of proposed business:

7 What size unit do you wish to occupy?

8 On what date would you like to occupy the unit?

9 What hours will your business be open?

10 Would you please indicate the following:

(a) Bankers:

Name ....

Address ....

....

Telephone ....

(b) Accountants:

Name ....

Address ....

....

Telephone ....

(c) Solicitors:

Name ....

Address ....

....

Telephone ....

(d) Insurance Brokers:

Name ....

Address ....

....

Telephone ....

11 Please give the name and address of an individual who can deputize for you in your absence:

Name ....

Address ....

....

Telephone ....

12 Please indicate which of the following you will require:

Electricity Plant — single-phase ☐
— three-phase ☐

Water and drainage — domestic supply only ☐

Heavy floor loading ☐

Secretarial service ☐

Marketing service ☐

13 Please indicate which of the following is applicable to your business:

Noise level minimal ☐
reasonable ☐
considerable ☐

Vibration level of any equipment minimal ☐
reasonable ☐
considerable ☐

Bibliography

This bibliography is not intended to be an exhaustive list of books and articles covering the subject of conversion and subdivision. The books included complement this text and will give readers different insights into the conversion and subdivision process.

Eley, P. and Worthington, J. (1984) *Industrial Rehabilitation: the use of redundant buildings for small enterprises,* Architectural Press, London

Green, D.H. and Foley, P.D. (1985) *Putting Spare Space to Work,* Small Business Research Trust, London

Green, D.H., Chalkley, B. and Foley, P.D. (1986) *How to Choose Business Premises,* Kogan Page, London

Marsh, P. (1983) *The Refurbishment of Commercial and Industrial Buildings,* Construction Press, London

Martinos, H. (1985) Workspace developments for small businesses. Ledis Review No. 1, The Planning Exchange, Glasgow

Segal, Quince Wicksteed (1985) Case studies of two managed workshop schemes: Avondale and Saltaire. A Report to the Department of Trade and Industry and Shell UK Ltd, HMSO, London

URBED (1981) Recycling industrial buildings, Capital Planning Information, Edinburgh

Index